THREATENED ANIMALS OF INDIA

THREATENED ANIMALS
OF INDIA

B. K. TIKADER

with a foreword by Dr. T. N. Khoshoo, Secretary,
Department of Environment, Government of India

ZOOLOGICAL SURVEY OF INDIA

Mahasaptami
13th October, 1983
Calcutta

Price

Indian : Rs. 150/00

Foreign : $ 45/00

£ 25/00

Published by the Director
Zoological Survey of India, Calcutta-700 012

Printed in India by
The Radiant Process, Calcutta

TO MY PARENTS
AND
MY FRIENDS, THE WILD ANIMALS OF INDIA

FOREWORD

Several unique species of plants and animals have disappeared in nature's own process of evolutionary change. However, in the recent past, many others have become extinct or are threatened by human activities caused by inadvertant actions or ignorance about the role of plants and animals in ecological balance. There is, however, growing concern throughout the world about the need for conservation of natural faunal and floral resources. This is indeed a very happy sign.

The Department of Environment has undertaken the task of identifying areas for designation as "Biosphere Reserves" which would serve as "ecological protectorates" of our biological wealth. It is in this context that the Department felt the need for a State-of-the-Art Report on the distribution of rare and threatened animals in different parts of our country with their pictorial representation, for easy recognition by laymen and Nature lovers in India. Last year, this task of preparing such a book was entrusted to the Zoological Survey of India, and I am indeed very glad that its Director, Dr. B. K. Tikader, has completed the same within a short time.

This book provides an overview of the problem with an inventory of five extinct and 141 threatened species of higher animals including their classification, habitats, factors threatening their existence, and wherever possible, necessary protective measures. This is the first attempt to consolidate material on the subject from diverse sources. I am sure that this publication will be of great value and use to all concerned for protection of our magnificient wildlife.

T. N. Khoshoo

Department of Environment
Government of India
New Delhi

(T. N. Khoshoo)
Secretary

CONTENTS

Page

Foreword
Preface
Acknowledgements
Introduction   1
Why conserve wildlife   2
Steps taken towards conservation   3
Work done in India on threatened species   5
Project Tiger   5
Gir Lion Sanctuary Project   6
Crocodile Breeding Project   6
Project Hangul   6
Himalayan Musk Deer Project   7
Manipur Browantlered Deer Project   7
Lesser cat Project   7
Contributions by The Zoological Survey of India   8
Population Census of Rhesus Macaque and Hanuman
    Langur of India   8
Eco-ethological Studies and Population Estimates of
    Cercopithecid Primates of Peninsular India   8
Study on the Population Ecology of the most Endangered Species of
    Mammals and Birds in the Arid Zone of India   9
Rare Species of Animals, their Categories and Definitions   9

MAMMALS

PRIMATES

Slender Loris	1.	*Loris tardigradus* (Linnaeus)	13
Slow Loris	2.	*Nycticebus coucang* (Boddaert)	16
Liontailed Macaque	3.	*Macaca silenus* (Linnaeus)	17
Pigtailed Macaque	4.	*Macaca nemestrina leonina* Blyth	19
Crabeating Macaque	5.	*Macaca fascicularis* (Raffles)	20
Stumptailed Macaque	6.	*Macaca arctoides* I. Geoffroy	23
Nilgiri Langur	7.	*Presbytis johni* (Fischer)	26
Capped Langur	8.	*Presbytis pileatus* (Blyth)	29
Golden Langur	9.	*Presbytis geei* Khajuria	30
Phayre's Leaf Monkey	10.	*Presbytis phayrei* Blyth	30
Hoolock Gibbon	11.	*Hylobates hoolock* (Harlan)	33

PHOLIDOTA

Chinese Pangolin	12.	*Manis pentadactyla aurita* Hodgson	36

Indian Pangolin 13. *Manis crassicaudata* Gray 37

CARNIVORA

Wolf 14. *Canis lupus* Linnaeus 39
Jackal 15. *Canis aureus* Linnaeus 41
Red Fox 16. *Vulpes vulpes* (Linnaeus) 42
Indian Fox 17. *Vulpes bengalensis* (Shaw) 43
Indian Wild Dog 18. *Cuon alpinus* (Pallas) 44
Brown Bear 19. *Ursus arctos isabellinus* Horsfield 45
Malayan Sun Bear 20. *Helarctos malayanus* (Raffles) 48
Sloth Bear 21. *Melursus ursinus* (Shaw) 49
Red Panda 22. *Ailurus fulgens* F. Cuvier 50
Ermine or Stoat 23. *Mustela erminea* Linnaeus 51
Ratel or Honey Badger 24. *Mellivora capensis* (Schreber) 53
Hog-Badger 25. *Arctonyx collaris* F. Cuvier 54
Malabar Civet 26. *Viverra megaspila* Blyth 55
Spotted Linsang 27. *Prionodon pardicolor* Hodgson 57
Binturong 28. *Arctictis binturong* (Raffles) 60
Crabeating Mongoose 29. *Herpestes urva* (Hodgson) 61
Striped Hyena 30. *Hyaena hyaena* (Linnaeus) 63
Jungle Cat 31. *Felis chaus* Güldenstaedt 64
Indian Desert Cat 32. *Felis silvestris ornata* Gray 65
Pallas's Cat 33. *Felis manul* Pallas 67
Golden Cat 34. *Felis temmincki* Vigors & Horsfield 68
Leopard Cat 35. *Felis bengalensis* Kerr 69
Rustyspotted Cat 36. *Felis rubiginosa* Geoffroy 71
Fishing Cat 37. *Felis viverrina* Bennett 73
Marbled Cat 38. *Felis marmorata charltoni* Gray 74
Lynx 39. *Felis lynx isabellina* Blyth 75
Caracal 40. *Felis caracal schmitzi* Matschie 76
Clouded Leopard 41. *Neofelis nebulosa* (Griffith) 79
Leopard or Panther 42. *Panthera pardus* (Linnaeus) 81
Tiger 43. *Panthera tigris* (Linnaeus) 82
Asiatic Lion 44. *Panthera leo persica* (Meyer) 84
Snow Leopard 45. *Panthera uncia* (Schreber) 85
Cheetah 46. *Acinonyx jubatus venaticus* (Griffith) 88

Page

PERISSODACTYLA

Great Onehorned Rhinoceros	47.	*Rhinoceros unicornis* Linnaeus	89
Lesser Onehorned Rhinoceros	48.	*Rhinoceros sondaicus* Desmarest	90
Asiatic Wild Ass	49.	*Asinus hemionus khur* (Lesson)	92
Kiang	50.	*Asinus kiang* (Moorcroft)	94

ARTIODACTYLA

Andaman Wild Pig	51.	*Sus scrofa andamanensis* Blyth	95
Pygmy Hog	52.	*Sus salvanius* (Hodgson)	97
Mouse Deer	53.	*Tragulus meminna* (Erxleben)	98
Musk Deer	54.	*Moschus moschiferus* Linnaeus	99
Swamp Deer	55.	*Cervus duvauceli* G. Cuvier	101
Manipur Thamin	56.	Cervus eldi eldi M'Clelland	104
Hangul	57.	*Cervus elaphus hanglu* Wagner	105
Fourhorned Antelope	58.	*Tetracerus quadricornis* (Blainville)	107
Gaur	59.	*Bos gaurus* H. Smith	108
Yak	60.	*Bos mutus* (Przewalski)	110
Wild Buffalo	61.	*Bubalus bubalis* (Linnaeus)	111
Blackbuck	62.	*Antilope cervicapra* (Linnaeus)	113
Tibetan Antelope or Chiru	63.	*Pantholops hodgsoni* (Abel)	116
Chinkara	64.	*Gazella dorcas* (Linnaeus)	117
Tibetan Gazelle	65.	*Procapra picticaudata* Hodgson	119
Takin	66.	*Budorcas taxicolor* Hodgson	120
Goral	67.	*Nemorhaedus goral* (Hardwicke)	122
Himalayan Tahr	68.	*Hemitragus jemlahicus* (H. Smith)	123
Nilgiri Tahr	69.	*Hemitragus hylocrius* (Ogilby)	125
Ibex	70.	*Capra ibex* Linnaeus	126
Markhor	71.	*Capra falconeri* (Wagner)	128
Nayan	72.	*Ovis ammon hodgsoni* Blyth	129
Urial	73.	*Ovis orientalis* Gmelin	131

Page

LAGOMORPHA

Hispid Hare   74.   *Caprolagus hispidus*
(Pearson)   133

RODENTIA

Grizzled Giant Squirrel   75.   *Ratufa macroura dandolena*
Thomas & Wroughton   134
Crestless Himalayan Porcupine   76.   *Hystrix hodgsoni* (Gray)   136

CETACEA

Blue Whale   77.   *Balenoptera musculus*
Linnaeus   137
Sperm Whale   78.   *Physeter catodon* Linnaeus   138
Common Dolphin   79.   *Delphinus delphis* Linnaeus   139
Gangetic Dolphin   80.   *Platanista gangetica*
(Lebeck)   140

SIRENIA

Sea Cow   81.   *Dugong dugon* (Müller)   141

BIRDS

CICONIIFORMES

Eastern White Stork   82.   *Ciconia ciconia boyciana*
Swinhoe   145

ANSERIFORMES

Large Whistling Teal   83.   *Dendrocygna bicolor*
(Vieillot)   146
Andaman Teal   84.   *Anas gibberifrons albogularis*
(Hume)   148
Pinkheaded Duck   85.   *Rhodonessa caryophyllacea*
(Latham)   150
Whitewinged Wood Duck   86.   *Cairina scutulata* (S. Muller)   152

FALCONIFORMES

Himalayan Golden Eagle   87.   *Aquila chrysaetos daphanea*
Severtzov   154

Page

Himalayan Bearded Vulture 88. *Gypaetus barbatus aureus*
(Hablizl) 157
Osprey 89. *Pandion haliaetus haliaetus*
(Linnaeus) 157
Shahin Falcon 90. *Falco peregrinus peregrinator*
Sundevall 159

GALLIFORMES

Nicobar Megapode 91. *Megapodius freycinet*
Gaimard 160
Pheasant-Grouse 92. *Tetraophasis szechenyii*
Madarasz 162
Assam Bamboo Partridge 93. *Bambusicola fytchii*
hopkinsoni Godwin-Austen 164
Mountain Quail 94. *Ophrysia superciliosa*
(J. E. Gray) 164
Blood Pheasant 95. *Ithaginis cruentus*
(Hardwicke) 166
Western Tragopan 96. *Tragopan melanocephalus*
(J. E. Gray) 168
Satyr Tragopan 97. *Tragopan satyra* (Linnaeus) 170
Blyth's Tragopan 98. *Tragopan blythii* (Jerdon) 172
Temminck's Tragopan 99. *Tragopan temminckii*
(J. E. Gray) 175
Himalayan Monal Pheasant 100. *Lophophorus impejanus*
(Latham) 177
Sclater's Monal Pheasant 101. *Lophophorus sclateri*
Jerdon 179
Elwes's Eared Pheasant 102. *Crossoptilon crossoptilon*
harmani Elwes 181
Koklass Pheasant 103. *Pucrasia macrolopha*
(Lesson) 183
Cheer Pheasant 104. *Catreus wallichii*
(Hardwicke) 184
Hume's Bartailed Pheasant 105. *Syrmaticus humiae humiae*
(Hume) 186
Peacock-Pheasant 106. *Polyplectron bicalcaratum*
(Linnaeus) 187
Indian Peafowl 107. *Pavo cristatus* Linnaeus 190

GRUIFORMES

Blacknecked Crane 108. *Grus nigricollis* Przevalski 191
Hooded Crane 109. *Grus monacha* Temminck 194
Siberian Crane 110. *Grus leucogeranus* Pallas 195

Masked Finfoot 111. *Heliopais personata*
(G. R. Gray) 196
Great Indian Bustard 112. *Ardeotis nigriceps* (Vigors) 198
Bengal Florican 113. *Eupodotis bengalensis
bengalensis* (Gmelin) 199
Lesser Florican 114. *Sypheotides indica*
(J. F. Miller) 202

CHARADRIIFORMES

Jerdon's Courser 115. *Cursorius bitorquatus*
(Blyth) 203
Indian Skimmer 116. *Rhyncops albicollis*
Swainson 205

COLUMBIFORMES

Nicobar Pigeon 117. *Caloenas nicobarica nicobarica*
(Linnaeus) 206

STRIGIFORMES

Great Horned Owl 118. *Bubo bubo* (Linnaeus) 208
Forest Spotted Owlet 119. *Athene blewitti* (Hume) 209

CAPRIMULGIFORMES

Ceylon Frogmouth 120. *Batrachostomus moniliger*
Blyth 211
Hodgson's Frogmouth 121. *Batrachostomus hodgsoni
hodgsoni* (G. R. Gray) 212

CORACIIFORMES

Assam Brownbacked Hornbill 122. *Ptilolaemus tickelli austeni*
(Jerdon) 213
Rufousnecked Hornbill 123. *Aceros nipalensis*
(Hodgson) 214
Assam Wreathed Hornbill 124. *Rhyticeros undulatus
ticehursti* Deignan 216
Narcondam Hornbill 125. *Rhyticeros (plicatus)
narcondami* (Hume) 218
Indian Pied Hornbill 126. *Anthracoceros malabaricus
malabaricus* Gmelin 220
Malabar Pied Hornbill 127. *Anthracoceros coronatus
coronatus* (Boddaert) 221

Page

Great Pied Hornbill 128. *Buceros bicornis homrai*
Hodgson 222.

REPTILES

TESTUDINES

Leatherback Turtle 129. *Dermochelys coriacea*
(Linnaeus) 227
Tortoiseshell Turtle 130. *Eretmochelys imbricata*
(Linnaeus) 228
Green Sea Turtle 131. *Chelonia mydas* (Linnaeus) 230
Olive Ridley Turtle 132. *Lepidochelys olivacea*
(Eschscholtz) 231
Batagur 133. *Batagur baska* (Gray) 233

CROCODYLIA

Gharial 134. *Gavialis gangeticus*
(Gmelin) 236
Estuarine Crocodile 135. *Crocodylus porosus*
Schneider 238
Mugger 136. *Crocodylus palustris*
(Lesson) 240

SQUAMATA

Water Monitor 137. *Varanus salvator* (Laurenti) 241
Common Indian Monitor 138. *Varanus bengalensis*
(Daudin) 243
Yellow Monitor 139. *Varanus flavescens* (Gray) 244
Indian Desert Monitor 140. *Varanus griseus* (Daudin) 246
Indian Rock Python 141. *Python molurus* (Linnaeus) 247
Reticulated Python 142. *Python reticulatus*
(Schneider) 248
Indian Eggeating Snake 143. *Elachistodon westermanni*
Reinhardt 251

AMPHIBIANS

URODELIA

Himalayan Newt 144. *Tylototriton verrucosus*
Anderson 252

ANURA

Malabar Tree Toad   145. *Nectophryne tuberculosa*
(Gunther)   254
Garo Hills Tree Toad   146. *Nectophryne kempi*
Boulenger   254

Bibliography   255

APPENDICES

I   Indian Board for Wild Life (IBWL)   257
II   Indian Wild Life (Protection) Act and its Schedules.   261
III   IUCN/WWF/WWF-India/FAO and UNDP.   270
IV   International Council for Bird Preservation (ICBP)   272
V   Convention on International Trade in Endangered Species of
Wild Fauna and Flora (CITES).   274
VI   Wildlife Sanctuaries and National Parks   285

PREFACE

Since the turn of the 20th century as many as three species of birds and two species of mammals have ceased to exist in India alone. Another three species of amphibians, fifteen species of reptiles, forty-four species of birds and seventy-nine species of mammals are today facing extinction. It is true that no animal or plant species is everlasting, and that none has yet existed for more than a few million years without evolving into something different or becoming extinct. This process is most usually slow in Nature but the pace of extinction of species in the recent times has been alarmingly swift. Wildlife, an important natural resource, appears to have borne the brunt of man's developmental activities. Not only has the population of individual species gone down alarmingly but also their habitat has either shrunk drastically or is being systematically made unfit for their existence. These strike at the very root of the ability of wildlife to renew and replenish itself by its own resource. This phenomenon can be directly or indirectly attributed to the ruthless and thoughtless exploitation of natural resources by man.

Although the matter of conservation of wildlife has been receiving the attention of the Government of India since the British times, a lot remains yet to be done. Since Independence a number of legislations have been enacted for conservation of wildlife, which do not seem to have proved effective, because of inadequate enforcement machinery and lack of appreciation by the general public. Even the literate intelligentia of the country exhibit a profound ignorance and apathy in this matter. Scientific researches on various problems of wildlife conservation still remain far from satisfactory.

One of the most important duties and responsibility of the Zoological Survey of India is to inculcate interest in and popularise the cause of wildlife conservation in our country. With the recent increasing awareness of the importance of wildlife, much publicity has been given for their protection, all of which in effect seem to have been confined to the elite urban people or learned biologists. The aim of this book is not only to serve the urban elite but also to cater to the educational interests of the rural folk, who are the real people to come in contact with the wildlife in day-to-day life. If this book can serve this purpose, its aim will be amply fulfilled. To make it readily understandable as many as 132 colour and one black and white photographs are included with brief descriptions and distribution maps of the mammals, birds, reptiles and amphibians as well as their present status. Interalia this book could also create an interest in the school children as well as in the college students, constituting the coming generation, who have to play the vital role in the preservation of our future wildlife.

The draft of this book was seen by Prof. Sivatosh Mookerjee, Chairman and by other members of the Scientific Programme Implementation & Evaluation Committee for the Zoological Survey of India. They share my view that the publication of this kind of popular book can drive public awareness towards the conservation of our dwindling wildlife and thus can help to save the fast deteriorating delicate balance of the natural ecosystem of our country.

I have included in this book, some mammals and birds namely, Cheetah, Lesser Onehorned Rhinoceros, Pinkheaded Duck, Jerdon's Courser and Mountain Quail, which are practically extinct from our country. There is no separate book to make the public aware about the extinct animals of India, therefore these have been included here with proper writeup, even though in the true sense these animals do not come under the purview of this book.

It is possible in a work like this there may be some inadequacies and there is always room for improvement. Readers are requested to bring to the attention of the author any suggestion in this direction.

Mahasaptami   B. K. TIKADER
13th October, 1983
Calcutta.

ACKNOWLEDGEMENTS

I am deeply indebted to the Hon'ble Prime Minister, Smt. Indira Gandhi, Chairperson, Indian Board for Wild Life, who has provided me the inspiration to write this book.

It is my great privilege to thank the Hon'ble Deputy Minister, Department of Environment, Sri Digvijay Sinh, who encouraged me to write this pictorial book, which will develop an awareness in people about the conservation of wildlife.

I also wish to express my deep sense of gratitude to Dr. T. N. Khoshoo, Secretary, Department of Environment for his personal interest in this book and for writing the foreword. It is only due to his constant help it has been possible to bring out this book within a short span of time.

Thanks are also due to Shri Samar Singh, Joint Secretary, Department of Environment and Wildlife, New Delhi and Prof. A. K. Sharma, University of Calcutta, for their constructive suggestions for improvement.

In the preparation of a book of this magnitude, the help of various individuals and institutions was needed and I offer my sincere thanks to all of them : to the Editor of the International Wild Life Encyclopedia for using some of their pictures; Shri J. C. Daniel, Curator, Bombay Natural History Society; Shri Hanumantha Rao; the authority of the World Wildlife Fund-India, Bombay; Shri S. P. Shahi, Ranchi, Bihar; Dr. Wang Sung, Institute of Zoology, Sinica, China; Dr. George Archibald, International Crane Foundation, U.S.A.; Mr. W. Rosser, U.S.A. and Mr. J. J. Buxton, England, for permitting me to use certain photographs. I am thankful to the Director, Zoological Garden, London; Shri Pushpa Kumar, Director, Zoological Park, Hyderabad; Shri, A. K. Das, Director, Alipur Zoological Garden, Calcutta; Dr. J. H. Desai, Director, National Zoological Park, New Delhi; authorities of the Zoological Garden, Gauhati, Zoological Garden, Jodhpur, Zoological Garden, Junagadh, Zoological Garden, Madras, Zoological Garden, Mysore, Kanha National Park, Madhya Pradesh; Shri R. Whitaker, Crocodile Bank Trust, Madras, and to Shri A. A. H. Khan, Zoological Garden, Port Blair, for providing me facilities to take the photographs of animals maintained under their custody or in the wild.

Thanks are also due to my colleagues of the Zoological Survey of India for assisting me in various ways in the preparation of this book : to Dr. K. C. Jayaram, Dr. V. C. Agrawal, Shri, P. K. Das, Shri R. K. Ghose, and Shri G. Sivagurunathan, who worked day and night with me for the completion of this book and it was not possible for me to achieve this target without their help within the specific time; to Dr. R. K. Kacker for his painstaking and enthusiastic efforts to bring some photographs from various sources in a short time; to Dr. R. C. Sharma and Shri Anurup Sarkar for providing valuable information; to Dr. B. S. Lamba from whom I received a few photographs; to Sarvashri Sitaram Mandal, S. K. Chanda, Arun Kumar Ghosh, Sankar Aich, D. Pyne, P. Biswas and Late Aswini Kumar Karmakar, Artists of our department, for sketching the distribution maps and some coloured illustrations; to Sarvashri Mrinal Sen, Abdul Basit, and Kanchan Dey for taking some of the photographs of animals and to Shri Anil Kumar Bhattacharjee, Stenographer, for typing the manuscript.

I must thank the proprietors of The Radiant Process namely, Shri Nirad Baran Mukherjee and Shri Sudhir Chandra Mukherjee and their working staff, who were engaged in printing this book. My thanks are also due to Shri Nirmal Banerjee, who worked tirelessly in processing the bromides of this book. I would also like to express my thanks to Shri Arup Kumar Ghose for his active help.

Last but not the least, I am thankful to Dr. Biswamoy Biswas, Emeritus Scientist, Zoological Survey of India, for kindly going through the manuscript and offering valuable suggestions and to my friends, Professor Amalesh Chowdhury, University of Calcutta, and Shri N. S. Chakravarthy, Chief Engineer, Posts and Telegraphs and my next door neighbour, for their manifold help; to Dr. A. K. Ghosh, Dr. O. B. Chhotani, Shri Bhanu Sinha, and my son, Shri Shyamal Tikader, who readily helped me in various ways.

The accomplishment of a task of this nature in a short time is impossible without a deep moral and spiritual support and guidance. These I received in abundant measure from Smt. Mohini Khoshoo.

Before I conclude I would like to thank my wife, Smt. Mridula Tikader but for whose unrelenting indulgences and patience with me, this book would never have made its journey to the press.

INTRODUCTION

In recent years there has been an increased desire to acquire greater knowledge about Nature, and more and more people are becoming more closely acquainted with the term "Wildlife", though there is no unanimous definition of it. In a broad sense, wildlife means plants and animals in their wild state, embracing all living organisms.

As India is a vast country, naturally, it exhibits a great variety of vegetation. The panorama of geographical variations and distinctions which range from the rain forests of Assam to the snows of the Himalaya and the deserts of Rajasthan, and from deciduous forests of central highlands to the mangrove swamps of Sundarbans, have their own typical faunal assemblage. These floral and faunal complexes have played vital role in the development of human culture from the dawn of civilisation. In the earliest stage, wildlife was a source of fuel, tool, food, clothing, folklore, religious belief, etc. But at that time more or less an equilibrium was maintained between man and the ecosystem. With the development of agriculture, some species were domesticated to serve man directly, others continued to be hunted for their meat, horns, skins, etc. and many more affected him indirectly through their role in the larger ecosystem of which he is only a part. As man became more and more civilised, his needs gradually increased. With the help of modern technology, he started to tap the various resources of the ecosystem carelessly and ceaselessly, without having the faintest idea as to its consequences. Thus the relationship between man and his ecosystem started to change with a rapid pace, resulting in the deterioration of the quality of the environment.

The human population explosion in the last few decades, demanding developments in various spheres, has resulted directly or indirectly in the sudden and often far-reaching disturbances in the several natural ecosystems in India. The rapid growth of urban areas, construction of dams and hydro-electric projects, buildings and roads, and encroachment on vast areas of forest lands for extension of agriculture and mining operation, are some examples of direct disturbances in our natural ecosystems. These imbalances in nature have posed problems for the survival of wildlife. Besides these, in order to satisfy human ego and human urge to establish supremacy over other life forms, man has driven certain species to a point of no return and many more are awaiting the same fate. Thus a nonrenewable resource of vital interest is being mindlessly squandered.

It is well known that several species of wild animals yield articles that have attractive overseas markets. The worst victims are no doubt, the fur-bearing mammals, birds with colourful and ornamental feathers, reptiles mainly crocodiles, snakes and monitors with fascinating skins, which are used in the manufacture of goods for fashionable sections of the society, all over the world. Elephants are hunted for ivory and the rhinoceroses for the horn, for making ornamental articles and for its medicinal property respectively. Some medicinal values of several species of animals and the inheritance of traditions and superstitions buttressed by ignorance, pose a serious threat to wildlife, which is difficult to combat.

It is heartening to note that the Government administrators and the naturalists have, lately, started to feel the pinch of the disturbances in our ecosystem, and are becoming conscious of the threat to the biosphere and its living components. Now efforts are under way to protect the same as far as possible. However, the best way of achieving it, is by arousing public consciousness.

Hence, the present book primarily aims at educating the general mass and arousing their sentiments towards the preservation of the biosphere including its rich wildlife, which in recent years, has been threatened due to our ignorance and apathy. This book further brings out general information on the rare and endangered species of mammals, birds, reptiles and amphibians, possible causes of their rarity, the steps taken for their protection and suggestions for future action.

In this book only higher vertebrates which are very conspicuous and familiar to common people are included. Apart from these, there are many kinds of fishes, molluscs, insects, corals, etc., which are also threatened and need conservation but will be accommodated in another book in future.

Why conserve wildlife : It may appear paradoxical if not wasteful to the average citizen to spend so much energy and money in conservation of wildlife, when the country is struggling for economic independence. What difference does it make, one may ask, if Cheetah and Pinkheaded Duck have disappeared, and the Tiger or the Lion would vanish tomorrow ? Like all other aspects, this attitude has its appeals and oppositions. Our honourable Prime Minister, Smt. Indira Gandhi in her message on the occasion of the inauguration of the "Tiger Project" on 1st April, 1973, answered this question very precisely. She said, "The narrow outlook of the accountant must give way to the wider vision of recreational, educational and ecological value of totally undisturbed areas of wilderness. Is it beyond our political will and administrative ingenuinity to set aside about one or two per cent of our forests in our pristine glory for this purpose?"

Our wildlife is the greatest heritage and in many ways more important than the Tajmahal or the Temples of Khajuraho, because, unlike these man-made structures, if once destroyed wildlife can never be restored. At the present rate of habitat destruction, overgrazing by domestic stock and hunting, there will be very little of wildlife left by the turn of the century. Our future generations could miss the majestic beauty of the tiger in the Sundarbans, the magnificent bison and the lordly elephant in Periyar, placidly grazing rhino among the reeds and grasses of Kaziranga, the elegant swamp deer of Kanha and the wonderful congregation of birds at the Keoladeo National Park, Bharatpur. If all these animals would cease to exist, then how dull would life be ? All this can and will happen, if proper conservation measures are not taken before it is too late.

Further, the life on earth is a delicate balance. Plants convert carbon dioxide of the air and water into organic matter with the help of chloroplasts in the presence of sunlight. Herbivores derive their energy from the plants, and the carnivores in their turn from the herbivores. There are also organisms called "decomposers" which release the energy back to nature, thus completing the cycle. We can, thus, see that producers, consumers and decomposers form food chains. The various food chains and cycles constitute the life support system essential for survival of the living world. Any major alteration in any one of these, results in serious disturbance in the balance of Nature and may threaten the very existence of man himself on this planet. To sustain life, renewability of the resources and life support systems should be maintained for endless duration, which in turn, demands an understanding of the ability of the species to adapt themselves to the changing environment and to integrate these considerations in the development of any planning process. This, in essence, is the crux of wildlife conservation.

Steps taken towards conservation : It is interesting to know how we have gradually developed the awareness of the protection of wildlife. At the turn of the twentieth century, people, perhaps with the idea that wildlife was inexhaustible, took pride in boasting of the number of trophies they had secured. The British rulers began to appreciate the importance of conservation of wildlife and enforced various Acts, e.g., the Rhino Protection Act, the Elephant Protection Act, the Arms Act, etc., from time to time to save rhinoceros, elephant and other wild animals from ruthless massacre. But the first concrete step towards it was taken soon after independence in 1952 with the setting up of a Central Board for Wildlife, which was subsequently renamed the Indian Board for Wildlife (IBWL). Soon most of the states also followed up. Inspite of the formation of these boards much could not be achieved as those concerned with conservation, worked in isolation, far removed from the mainstream of planning process. Indeed we owe greatly to late Pandit Jawaharlal Nehru, a lover of nature and to his illustrious daughter Smt. Indira Gandhi, who is the present Chairman of the Indian Board for Wildlife, for highlighting the values of our wildlife and the need for its conservation.

The Indian Board for Wildlife is the main advisory board for advising the

Government of India regarding wildlife policy in the country. The Director, Zoological Survey of India, the Director, Botanical Survey of India and the State Chief Conservators of Forests are ex-officio members of this Board. It has many specialised wings like the Zoo Wing, the Bird Wing and the Flora Wing for making appropriate recommendations to the IBWL. Some of its important achievements are the enacting of Wildlife (Protection) Act, 1972, establishment of national parks, sanctuaries and zoological gardens, promoting public interest and education in wildlife and its products, formulation of a national environmental conservation policy, revision of the national forest policy, etc.

To restrict and regulate the thriving global trade in endangered species, India became a party to the International Convention on Trade in Endangered Species of Wild Fauna and Flora (CITES) in 1976. Under the convention, the Inspector General of Forests and the Director of Wildlife Preservation have been designated as the Management Authority, supported by the scientific authorities namely, the Director, Zoological Survey of India, the Director, Botanical Survey of India and the Director, Central Marine Fisheries Research Institute. To control the trade in endangered species, four Assistant Directors of Wildlife have been appointed at the four international airports of the country viz., Bombay, Calcutta, Delhi and Madras, from where wildlife and its products can now be exported or imported, only after proper inspection.

In recent years many of the International Bodies like International Union for Conservation of Nature and Natural Resources (IUCN), World Wildlife Fund Internationale (WWF) and International Council for Bird Preservation (ICBP) have come up for purposes of safeguarding conservation, management and creation of awareness, and India is a member of all these bodies.

For effective conservation of wildlife, three basic needs namely (1) adequate food and water (2) place of refuge and (3) place to breed in safety, should be fulfilled. To achieve this, the following measures are in practice.

1.   Reserved forests, national parks and sanctuaries are left unexploited; where total unexploitation is not possible, the cutting operation of the forests is done in limited blocks at a time.

2.   Growing of a single variety of plant is discouraged as far as possible. Instead mixed vegetation is encouraged.

3.   Natural openings of the forest, waterholes and river sides are guarded against poachers.

4.   Controlled burning of grassland to increase forage and to preserve organic materials in the soil, is done in blocks, with unburnt area in between.

5.   Provisions for dust baths and artificial salt licks are made in the forests for maintaining the normal health of animals.

6.   Grazing of domestic live stock is dangerous to wild animals, as the latter can never compete successfully with the domestic stock. Moreover, the domestic stock may be responsible for transmitting several contagious diseases. Hence, grazing by domestic stock in protected areas is avoided as far as possible.

7.   Cultivation near the sanctuaries is also avoided to prevent ecological hazards due to pesticides.

8.   Scientific studies by qualified personnel on threatened species of animals are encouraged in order to assess and improve their status, even by breeding them in captivity and rehabilitating them in suitable habitats.

Several such measures have been undertaken and many more are needed to halt the decline of wildlife and to create conditions in which it can flourish with its diversity in natural settings, but nothing could be fruitful without educational and publicity programmes for a change in the human outlook, especially in the school-children who are the builders of future society. There is a general lack of knowledge in the conservation of nature and the value of wildlife in our country. Nature has been treated as a milch cow. Anything of use to man is exploited indiscriminately, inevitably leading to its depletion, sometimes beyond redemption. Ecology, till recently a word in the dictionary and now a fashion in vogue among scientific circles, found no place in modern development for several decades. Unless economy is tempered by ecology, there is no possibility of halting the present trend.

To sum up, the only permanent solution to the problems of protection of wildlife, which is a part of the macro-problem of protection of biosphere and its component ecosystems, lies in proper understanding of the living world and in the reorientation of the human outlook.

WORK DONE IN INDIA ON THREATENED SPECIES SPONSORED BY IUCN/WWF

A number of projects are being run currently in India to conserve various species of wildlife. These projects are being discussed below.

Project Tiger : On the recommendations of a Task Force of Indian Board for Wild Life, this project was initiated as a Central Sector Scheme in 1973, with nine tiger reserves located in different habitat types. To this, two more reserves were, subsequently, added, raising the tally to 11 reserves, covering an area of about 15800 sq km which forms 2.10 per cent of the total forest area and 0.49 per cent of the geographical area of the country.

The tiger reserves are located at Manas (Assam), Sunderbans (West Bengal), Palamau (Bihar), Simlipal (Orissa), Kanha (Madhya Pradesh), Corbett (Uttar Pradesh), Sariska and Ranthambhor (Rajasthan), Melghat (Maharashtra), Bandipur (Karnataka) and Periyar (Kerala). As a result of effective protection and phenomenal improvement in the habitat condition, there has been an increase in the population of all species of the prey and the predator. The population of tigers in nine tiger reserves, estimated at 268 in 1972 has increased to 757 in eleven reserves in 1981.

The Gir Lion Sanctuary Project : Gir Lion Sanctuary is located in Gujarat and is the last stronghold of the lion *(Panthera leo persica)* in Asia. The project was initiated in 1972. At that time, the area of the sanctuary was 1265.01 sq km, which was, subsequently, increased to 1412.12 sq km in 1974. The central core portion of the Gir Sanctuary covering an area of 258.71 sq km was declared as a National Park. The improvement of habitat and minimising disturbances by human beings have resulted in the increase in the lion population from 180 in 1974 to 205 in 1979.

Crocodile Breeding Project : The three species of crocodiles, namely the Gharial *Gavialis gangeticus,* the Mugger, *Crocodylus palustris* and the Salt-Water Crocodile, *Crocodylus porosus* became rare in India by 1971. With a view to conserving these species, the Government of India approached U.N.D.P. for assistance. Following a consultancy visit report by Dr. H. R. Bustard, an F.A.O. expert on crocodile breeding and management, the work on this project was started in Orissa from 1st April, 1975. Subsequently, this scheme was extended to Uttar Pradesh (1975), Rajasthan (1975), West Bengal (1976), Tamil Nadu (1976), Andhra Pradesh (1977-78), Gujarat (1977), Kerala (1977), Madhya Pradesh (1978-79), Maharashtra (1979), Andaman Islands (1979), Assam (1979), Bihar (1979) and Nagaland (1980). During a five years period i.e., from 1976 to 1980, about 2700 gharials, 600 saltwater crocodiles and 900 muggers have been hatched at project rearing stations and a total of 710 crocodiles (324 gharials, 168 saltwater crocodiles and 218 muggers) were released into the wild. Crocodiles are being managed in twelve sanctuaries specially declared under the project. These sanctuaries are Bhiterkanika, Hadgarh and Satkosia Gorge in Orissa; Katerniaghat in Uttar Pradesh; Krishna, Lanjumaduga, Manjira, Papikonda, Coringa and Nagarjunasagar — Sri Sailam in Andhra Pradesh; Bhagabatpur in West Bengal and the National Chambal Sanctuary, spread over portions of Madhya Pradesh, Uttar Pradesh and Rajasthan. In addition to these, a number of private breeding farms have also been started. One of these is the Crocodile Bank Trust, Madras, which was started in 1975 under the able guidance of Mr. R. Whitaker, and is doing a commendable job.

Project Hangul : Hangul *(Cervus elaphus hanglu)* is a subspecies of the European Red Deer, and occurs in India in Jammu and Kashmir and Himachal Pradesh. The main concentration of this deer is in Dachigam Sanctuary. Unfortunately, Hangul has become rare since independence, due chiefly to poaching and habitat destruction. From an estimated number of 3000 in 1940, it was reduced to 140 – 170 in 1970. It was in the same year that the Hangul Project was launched by the IUCN/WWF/ State of Jammu and Kashmir under the expert guidance of Dr. Fred Kurt. The implementation of the Management-cum-Ecological Plan which envisages amongst other things, total protection against grazing by domestic animals in the sanctuary and habitat destruction, improvement of fodder and immunity from diseases, has yielded results and the population of this deer gradually increased to 320 in 1978 and to 347 in March 1980.

Himalayan Musk Deer Project : The Himalayan Musk Deer was once a widespread form, occuring along the Himalaya from Pakistan to Burma, and Tibet and southwestern China. The over-all range of the species might have changed a little, but intense burning and human interference in its habitat, have restricted the population to some isolated pockets, in India. As a part of the Threatened Deer Programme of the IUCN, a project was launched by WWF with the cooperation of the Government of India to undertake an ecological study of the Musk Deer in order to identify its conservation requirements. The project was started in Kedarnath Sanctuary, Uttar Pradesh. Besides protecting the musk deer within national parks and sanctuaries, there are plans to breed them in captivity and to reintroduce them into the wild.

The Manipur Browantlered Deer *(Cervus eldi eldi)* **Project** : The Manipur Browantlered Deer locally called 'Sangai', is one of the rarest and most localised mammals in the world. By 1950, this subspecies was regarded as extinct till located once again in a small area known as Keibul Lamjao at the south-eastern corner of the Logtak Lake. This area was first declared as a sanctuary in 1954 and, subsequently, as a national park in 1977. It covers an area of about 35 sq km. Though the area of the park is large, the real habitat of the deer does not exceed 15 sq. km. From an estimated number of 100 deer in 1960, it was reduced to 18 in 1977. However, a recent census in 1978 conducted by the Forest Department of Manipur showed a slight increase to 23 Sangai in the National Park. Besides this, there are another 49 in captivity in different zoos.

Lesser Cats Project : Several species of lesser cats inhabit India in varying ecological conditions and habitats. Their numbers for various reasons, are getting smaller and smaller over the years, so much so that four species, namely the Leopard Cat *(Felis bengalensis* Kerr*)*, the Marbled Cat *(Felis marmorata* Martin *)*, the Golden Cat *(Felis temmincki* Vigors & Horsfield*)* and the Fishing Cat *(Felis viverrina* Bennett*)*, are regarded as vulnerable in eastern India. In view of this, the WWF-India has launched a project called "Status Survey of the Lesser Cats in Eastern India" covering the States of Sikkim, West Bengal, Arunachal Pradesh, Assam, Meghalaya, Nagaland, Manipur, Tripura and Mizoram, in collaboration with the Zoological Survey of India. The ultimate aim of the project is to assess the population abundance

7

of the above-mentioned species, factors responsible for their decimation and to formulate conservation measures for them.

The project has, initially, started with a 'Pilot Survey of the four species of Lesser Cats in Sikkim and northern parts of West Bengal to achieve an overview of their status, recognize the area of their abundance, their ecological requirements, etc. and to develop a methodology for future surveys'.

According to preliminary assessments, the Leopard Cat is more common in Sikkim than in northern West Bengal, the Marbled Cat and the Golden Cat are rare both in Sikkim and West Bengal and the Fishing Cat is elusive at both the places.

CONTRIBUTION BY THE ZOOLOGICAL SURVEY OF INDIA

Population Census of Rhesus Macaque and Hanuman Langur of India : The importance of nonhuman primates in biomedical research and excessive demand for monkeys, particularly of the rhesus macaque by foreign countries, have put a heavy strain on the monkey population in India. The fear expressed in scientific circles that the rhesus population is on the decline, generated the necessity for ascertaining the current population status of Indian nonhuman primates. The survey revealed that Rhesus Macaque is found throughout northern India, the southern limit being Tapti river in the southwest and Darsi (Nellore District, Andhra Pradesh) in the southeast. The Hanuman Langur occurs throughout India, the eastern limit being Tista river in West Bengal. The estimated population of the former was found to be around 1,80,000 and that of the latter around 2,30,000. The study revealed that there is a real decline in the population of Rhesus Macaque in most parts of the country. However, concentration of its population is now confined in three states namely Uttar Pradesh, Andhra Pradesh and Tripura. The langurs are in abundance in Rajasthan, Uttar Pradesh, Madhya Pradesh, Bihar, Orissa, West Bengal, Maharashtra and Andhra Pradesh. Habitat-wise they are concentrated in forest habitat more than in any other habitat — 50.04% of rhesus and about 68.63% of langur occupy the forest belt.

Eco-ethological Studies and Population Estimates of Cercopithecid Primates of Peninsular India : Due to the reasons mentioned above, the census estimation of the rural and urban populations of three species of monkeys, namely, the Bonnet Macaque, *Macaca radiata* (Geoffroy), the Rhesus Macaque, *Macaca mulatta* (Zimmermann) and the Hanuman Langur, *Presbytis entellus* (Dufresne) was made in four southern states of India, viz., Andhra Pradesh, Tamil Nadu, Karnataka and Kerala. The estimated population came to be around 1,74,000 for Bonnet Macaque, 48,000 for Rhesus Macaque and 88,000 for Hanuman Langur. Out of the four states, the Rhesus Macaque is only confined to Andhra Pradesh. The Bonnet Macaque and the Hanuman Langur occur in all the four states but their concentration is more in Andhra Pradesh and Karnataka. The northernmost limit of distribution of the Bonnet Macaque in Andhra Pradesh is Vijayawada in the east and southern Hyderabad and Mehboobnagar in the west. The Hanuman Langur is absent in the coastal districts of Kerala where it is mostly confined to forests. The demographic parameters displayed by the populations of each species have been studied and discussed and so also the various environmental and sociological factors impinging on their population ecology.

A detailed two years simultaneous study of the ecology and behaviour of the Lion-tailed Macaque, *Macaca silenus* (Linnaeus) in Kerala was another major highlight of the programme.

Study on the Population Ecology of the most Endangered Species of Mammals and Birds in the Arid Zone of India : The population ecology of two threatened species of mammals, namely, the Indian Wild Ass, *Asinus hemionus khur* Lesson and the Desert Cat, *Felis silvestris ornata* Gray and a species of bird *viz.,* the Great Indian Bustard, *Ardeotis nigriceps* (Vigors), which are found in western India was studied. Pockets of their concentration were located and ecological studies made. The Indian Wild Ass has been located in Surendranagar district and in the Little Rann of Kutch in Gujarat, and the present population is estimated to be around 800. Similar pockets of concentration have been pin-pointed for the Great Indian Bustard in Shakalia Wildlife Sanctuary, Ajmer and Dham Singh Ki Dhani as well as many other localities in Jaisalmer. Its estimated population has increased from 700 to 900. The Desert Cat has been observed in the districts of Barmer and Jaisalmer.

RARE SPECIES OF ANIMALS, THEIR CATEGORIES AND DEFINITIONS

The following categories of rare animals have been recognised by the IUCN, based mainly on (1) the present and past distribution, (2) decline in number of populations in course of time, (3) abundance and quality of natural habitats and (4) biology and potential value of the species. These are defined as follows for purposes of conservation :

Endangered (E) : The taxa in danger of extinction and whose survival is unlikely if the casual factors continue operating. These are taxa whose numbers have been reduced to a critical level or whose habitats have been so drastically reduced that they are deemed to be in immediate danger of extinction.

Vulnerable (V) : The taxa likely to move into the endangered category in the near future if the casual factors continue operating. These are taxa of which most or all of the populations are decreasing because of over-exploitation, extensive destruction of habitat or other environmental disturbances; taxa with populations that have been seriously depleted and whose ultimate security is not yet assured; and taxa with populations that are still abundant but are under threat from serious adverse factors throughout their range.

Rare (R) : The taxa with small populations in the world that are not at present endangered or vulnerable, but are at risk. These taxa are usually localized within restricted geographical areas or habitats or are thinly scattered over a more extensive range.

Threatened (T) : The term "threatened" is used in the conservation context for species which are in one of the three categories *viz*, Endangered, Vulnerable or Rare.

Out of danger (O) : The taxa formerly included in one of the above categories but which are now considered relatively secure because effective conservation measures have been taken or the previous threat to their survival has been removed.

Indeterminate (I) : The taxa that are suspected of belonging to one of the first three categories, but for which insufficient information is currently available.

"A threat to any species of plant and animal life is a threat to Man himself".

— Indira Gandhi

MAMMALS

Order Primates

SLENDER LORIS

1. Loris tardigradus (Linnaeus)   (V)

The Slender Loris, as the name signifies, is a small, slender-bodied primate, much like the Slow Loris in appearance. However, its lean, lankey appearance, long limbs, a well-developed index finger and large ears are distinctive. The length of head and body measures 20-25 cm. The tail is absent. Its colour is dark grey or earthy brown with an embellishment of silvery hair.

Distribution : The species is known from southern India and Sri Lanka. In the Indian range of its occurrence, it is so far known from parts of Tamil Nadu, Karnataka, Kerala and southern Andhra Pradesh.

Habits and habitat : It is secretive in nature and remains hidden among foliage during the day time. It starts its rambles at dusk and moves from one tree to the other. Its nocturnal activity is not only confined to dense forest, but also to open tree jungle, and often visits bushes for feeding. It enjoys berries of *Lantana* and also feeds on insects, tree-frogs, lizards, and small birds. Newly born young ones have been seen in March, May, June and October.

Status : Half a century ago the Slender Loris was quite common. A large number of them were killed in many places for medicinal use in eye diseases. Moreover, it is also used as an experimental animal by various research institutions in South India. At present it is vulnerable due to habitat-destruction and unauthorised trapping to meet the requirements of local institutions and private bodies.

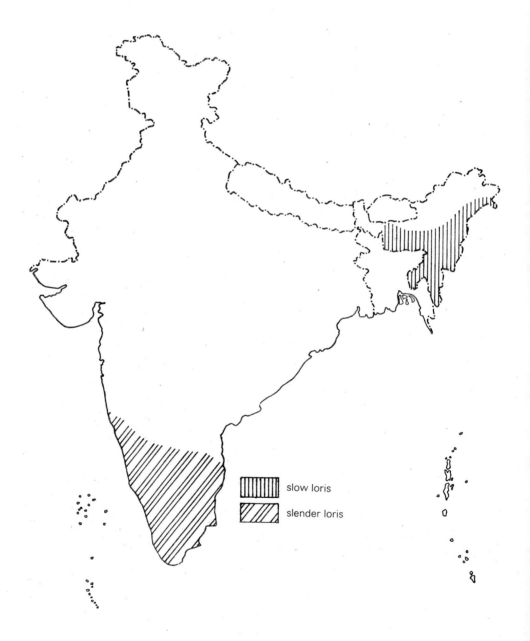

slow loris

slender loris

slender loris

slow loris

SLOW LORIS

2. **Nycticebus coucang** (Boddaert)   (V)

The body and the limbs of the Slow Loris are stout. It has a rounded head, and round eyes encircled with dark brown. In the head and body length it measures 30-40 cm. The tail is rudimentary. It has dense fur and is variable in body colour, silvery white on the head and shoulder and grey on the flanks and rump. A brown stripe is present on the middle of its back, terminating on the crown. Its second toe is clawed and the other toes are provided with flat nails.

Distribution : This species is an inhabitant of tropical rain forest south of the Brahmaputra river in northeastern India and also occurs in eastern Bangladesh and Burma to Far East. However, there is a solitary report of its occurrence from Goalpara, north of the Brahmaputra.

Habits and habitat :·The Slow Loris is a very seclusive nocturnal animal. It·is arboreal and seldom comes to the ground. It generally keeps to the forests, sleeping during the day time in holes or crevices of trees and coming forth at night for feeding. It feeds mainly on leaves, young shoots, fruits and insects. Nothing in particular is known about the breeding habit of this animal.

Status : It is seldom noticed due to its seclusive and nocturnal habits. The status of this species is vulnerable due to destruction of its habitat.

LIONTAILED MACAQUE

3. **Macaca silenus** (Linnaeus)   (E)

The Liontailed Macaque, with a lengthened face, is baboon-like in appearance. It is distinguished by the presence of a dark grey or brownish grey ruff surrounding the temples and the cheeks. The colour of the body and the face is black. It is of stocky built and measures 50-60 cm in the head and body length. The tail is short (25-40 cm), with a tuft of hair at the tip.

liontailed macaque

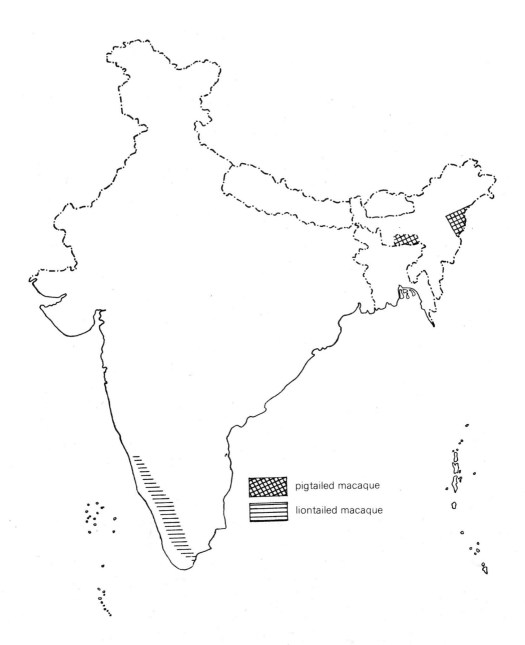

pigtailed macaque

liontailed macaque

18

Distribution : It once used to occur approximately from 14°N lat. to the extreme southern end of India along the Western Ghats. At present the known southernmost limit is 11°30' N lat., and more or less confined to the Nilgiri, Anaimalai and Cardamom Hills, Periyar Lake, etc. The northernmost record is a sighting at Anshi Ghat (c 15°N lat.) between Kadra and Kumbhawada in Karnataka in 1955.

Habits and habitat : The Liontailed Macaque is gregarious. It is a native of the undisturbed, evergreen, dense forest at elevations of 610-1070 m in the Western Ghats, and prefers tall trees of 20 m or more in height. With its dark colouring and shy and seclusive habits it is seldom seen. It feeds on fruits, buds and leaves of indigenous plants. New born young ones are noticed in September.

Status : Shrinkage of the preferred habitat of this macaque has brought considerable decrease in its population in the last 60 years or so. Modified land use for agriculture, extension of coffee and tea plantation and replacement of endemic forest trees by exotic species (viz. Eucalyptus, Wattle, etc.), are the major factors for reduction in its number. Direct interference by hunting it for fur trade and the supposed aphrodisiac properties of its meat have also added to its population decline.

PIGTAILED MACAQUE

4. Macaca nemestrina leonina Blyth (R)

The Pigtailed Macaque is a stout monkey, measuring c 50 cm in the head and body length and has long and powerful limbs. Its head is broad and rather flat with hair radiating from the centre of the crown. A V-shaped stripe is present over the forehead. The colour on the upper surface is dark brown or black with sides comparatively lighter and the underparts greyer. Its tail is pig-like, black above and light yellowish brown below and measures 17-20 cm in length.

Distribution : This macaque is reported from northeastern India and also from Burma, Yunnan (China), Thailand, southern Laos, southern Vietnam and possibly Kampuchea.

Habits and habitat : This species frequents evergreen forest at the base of hills and at elevations ranging from c 75 to 1300 m. Its food consists mainly of fruits, although leaves, caterpillars, insects and rice are also taken. It breeds twice during June and December.

Status : In India this monkey was rarely encountered, and now has become even rarer. The only recent record of its occurrence within India is the three specimens captured in Mawsynram area, Khasi Hills, Meghalaya, and sighting of a troop of 26 individuals in Hollongapar forest near Jorhat, Sibsagar district, Assam.

pigtailed macaque

CRABEATING MACAQUE

5. **Macaca fascicularis** (Raffles)   (V)

The Crabeating Macaque is a dusky or fawn coloured monkey, measuring about 50 cm in the head and body length. It superficially resembles the Bonnet Macaque of southern India, but is slightly larger. The hair on the crown, however, grow backwards from the brow as in the Rhesus Macaque. It has a very long tail, a little shorter than the head and body.

crabeating macaque

Nicobar Islands

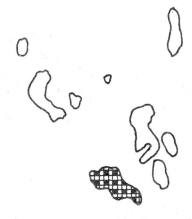

crabeating macaque

stumptailed macaque

NILGIRI LANGUR

7. **Presbytis johni** (Fischer)   (V)

The Nilgiri Langur is almost the size of the Common Langur, and measures about 80 cm in the head and body length; the females are a little smaller than the males. The general body colour is glossy black, with a yellowish brown head. The hair on the head are long and non-radiating. Its tail is long and subequal to the length of the head and body. The rump and the base of the tail are sometimes grizzled.

Distribution : This langur is known from the Western Ghats in India, ranging from Coorg (Karnataka) through Nilgiri and Palni Hills (Tamil Nadu) to Anaimalai, Brahmagiri and Cardamom Hills (Kerala).

Habits and habitat : This species is found in the tropical moist deciduous forest, where it lives in the sholas (strips of forest surrounded by grassland which is transected with a narrow water course) and the evergreen forest at elevations ranging from 900 to 1200 m, with trees up to 20 m in height, in small troops of 5-16 individuals. Early mornings and late evenings are its usual foraging hours, and feeds mainly on tree tops. Its food comprises fruits, leaves, shoots, etc., and it occasionally invades gardens and cultivated woodland.

Status : The population of this langur has become scarce in many areas where it was well known fifty to seventy years ago. At present the species is vulnerable due to the destruction of its natural habitat (the sholas) for cultivation and human settlements, and the construction of hydro-electric projects. In addition, the monkey is persecuted for its fur and alleged aphrodisiac property of its flesh. Census conducted during 1968-71 in South Coimbatore Forest Division in Tamil Nadu recorded 80 troops and in the Periyar Sanctuary (Kerala) about 100 troops.

CAPPED LANGUR

8. **Presbytis pileatus** (Blyth)   (V)

The Capped Langur is robust in built, measuring 60-71 cm in the head and body length and 76-102 cm in the length of tail; the females are smaller than the males. Its crown is covered with long, harsh hair, directed

nilgiri langur

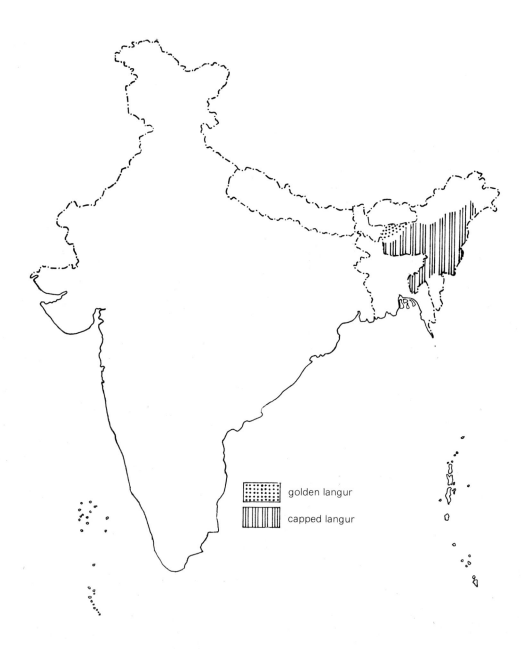

golden langur

capped langur

backwards from the forehead to form a cap. The hair on the cheeks are long and partly cover the ears. The colour of its back is dusky grey to ashy grey, and the middle portion of the back, the hands and the feet and occasionally the crown are dark brown or black. The ventral surface, cheeks and the sides of the neck are pale fulvous to golden brown. Its tail is dark brown and the face black.

Distribution : This langur occurs in northeastern India and is also found in Bangladesh and northern Burma.

Habits and habitat : The family life of this langur is very similar to that of the Common Langur. It inhabits dense and secluded tropical and secondary forests intersected by streams, at altitudes ranging from 60 to 1527 m. Its food consists of fruits, flowers and leaves. It is a shy and wary animal, and when scared hides behind foliage. It breeds during winter.

capped langur

Status : Exact status of this langur is unknown, but it is widely distributed and thriving well in the forests of northeastern India. However, it is vulnerable due to disturbances in the habitat at various places of its occurrence.

GOLDEN LANGUR

9. **Presbytis geei** Khajuria (V)

The Golden Langur is a rich golden to cream buff coloured langur with entirely black face, measuring *c* 48-50 cm in the head and body length. Hair on the flanks are longer and reddish. An ill-developed half whorl is present on the forehead, with hair radiating backwards and sideways. Its tail is slightly tassellated and measures about 76 cm in length.

Distribution : This Langur is distributed in the Himalayan foothills along Assam-Bhutan border between Sankosh and Manas rivers in India and Bhutan.

Habits and habitat : It lives in mixed deciduous forests, and is non-aggressive, docile and diurnal. The peak of its diurnal activities are recorded in the early mornings and evenings. It mates between December and February, and the young ones are born during September-November.

Status : Though presumed to be rare since its discovery, recent records indicate that the Golden Langur is thriving well and is abundant in the forests of central Bhutan. However, the limited range of its occurrence makes it highly vulnerable and susceptible to biotic interference that may result from modified land use that has already started in the range of its distribution.

PHAYRE'S LEAF MONKEY

10. **Presbytis phayrei** Blyth (V)

The Phayre's Leaf Monkey is a dark ashy brown langur, measuring 60-62 cm in the head and body length and about 75 cm in the length of tail. It is darker on the head, extremities and the tail tip. Its back from shoulders to loin is silvery. The underparts are whitish. The face is black except the lips and the area around the mouth and eyes which are white.

golden langur

phayre's leaf monkey

Distribution : This langur is mainly distributed in Burma and Thailand. Its western limit of occurrence is Tripura hills in India and the eastern hill region of Bangladesh.

Habits and habitat : This langur is found in small or large troops throughout Tripura in deciduous forest. Its average group size is 11. Its preferred habitat is bamboo and banana plantations on the hillsides in the vicinity of streams. It is a very shy animal and keeps itself hidden in the branches of trees. Its food consists of leaves, flowers and fruits. Breeding season of this Leaf Monkey appears to be in winter, and a single young is produced at birth.

Status : The population of this langur in India is not only localised but is also scanty. About 400 individuals comprising 36 groups have been counted by scientists of the Zoological Survey of India. Due to its localised distribution it is vulnerable and susceptible to modified land use, resulting in the reduction of its preferred habitat.

HOOLOCK GIBBON

11. **Hylobates hoolock** (Harlan) (V)

The Hoolock Gibbon is the only ape found in India. It is slender-bodied and tailless. The head and body measures 90-94 cm in length. It has a small and round head, with whitish band across the eyebrows. Its arms are very long, and are more than double the length of the legs. The nostrils are widely spaced and snout is not protruding. Males and the young females are black; mature females are yellowish grey.

Distribution : This gibbon is an inhabitant of dense forests of north-eastern India, south and east of the Brahmaputra and luhit rivers; it also occurs in eastern Bangladesh, northern Burma and Yunnan in China.

Habits and habitat : The Hoolock Gibbon usually lives in evergreen, semi-evergreen and moist deciduous forests mainly along the hill slopes in small family parties, in a definite territory. Its family size is small and normally consists of 2 to 4 individuals including the young ones. It is diurnal and more agile than the other apes. At night it remains in the forests in the valleys and at dawn ascends the hill sides to sun itself on the tree tops. It spends most of its time in feeding during early mornings and in the evenings. The network of paths made by this gibbon through the tree-tops can be traced by the worn out branches. Its main food items are leaves, twigs, flowers, fruits and even insects. The male is monogamous in habit and

hoolock gibbon (male)

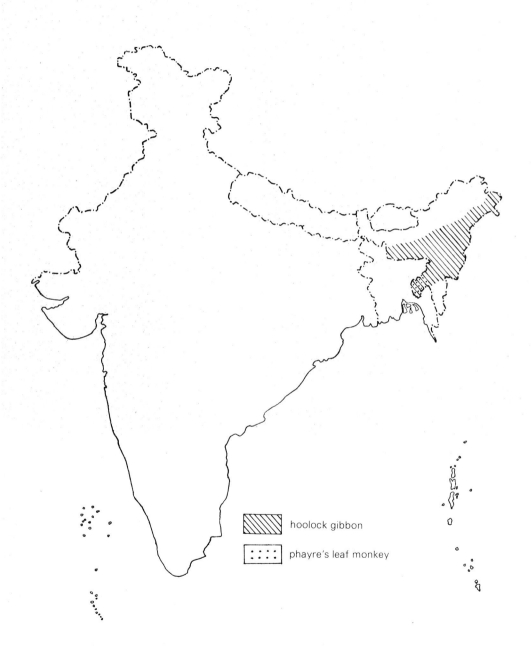

hoolock gibbon

phayre's leaf monkey

remains content with a particular female. The mating time is early in the rainy season and the young is born in winter, generally between December and March.

Status : Due to the destruction of pristine forests, the population of the Hoolock Gibbon is going down in the habitat preferred by it at a fast rate. The population of this ape has also been greatly affected due to killing by the tribals for flesh. A population estimate made in 1971-72 gave its total number as 78,700 in Assam, Meghalaya and Mizoram. However, according to the studies made by scientists of the Zoological Survey of India from 1976 to 1983, the actual number is much less.

Order Pholidota

CHINESE PANGOLIN

12. Manis pentadactyla aurita Hodgson   (I)

The Chinese Pangolin is more or less slender. The length of its head and body is 48-58 cm and that of the tail 33-38 cm. The upper side of the body, the tail, and the outer side of the limbs are covered with large overlapping scales. The undersurface of the body is clothed with coarse,

chinese pangolin

bristly hair. A few such hair also grow between the dorsal scales. There are 15 to 18 longitudinal rows of scales around the body. A well-developed ear-conch is present. The forefoot is furnished with long, somewhat curved and blunt claws for digging.

Distribution : The Chinese Pangolin occurs from Nepal to northeastern India, Burma, Laos and southern China.

Habits and habitat : This species inhabits forests as well as hilly countries. It is nocturnal in habit and spends the day curled up in a self-dug burrow of variable length. While walking, its front toes are bent under the soles. Its food consists of eggs and the adults of termites and ants. Though terrestrial in habit, it is often seen on trees in quest of tree ants. Nothing specially is known about its breeding habit, but it appears to be very much similar to that of the Indian Pangolin.

Status : Indeterminate. Due to its nocturnal habit, it is rarely seen. Tribals believe that its flesh and scales have great medicinal value, and as such random killing has reduced its population.

INDIAN PANGOLIN

13.   Manis crassicaudata Gray   (I)

The Indian Pangolin is very similar to the Chinese Pangolin but is a little larger. Its head and body measures 60-75 cm in length and the tail about 45 cm. The number of longitudinal rows of scales around the body vary from 11 to 13 and the scales are larger. The ear-conch is less prominent.

indian pangolin

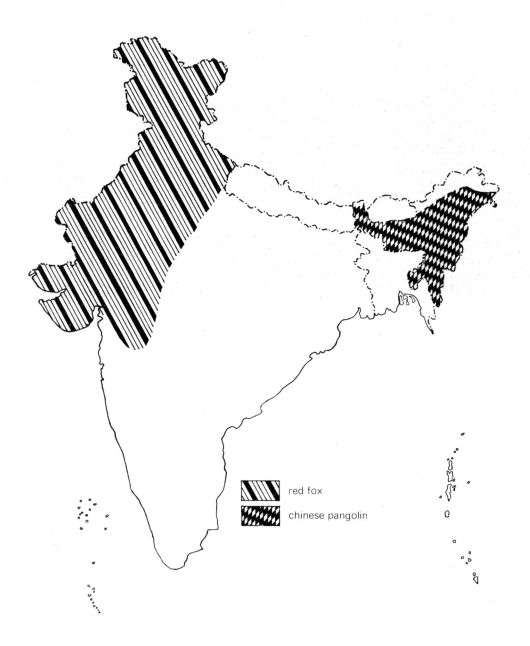

red fox

chinese pangolin

38

Distribution : It is widely distributed through the plains and lower slopes of hills from south of the Himalaya to the southern extremity of India and is also found in Sri Lanka.

Habits and habitat : The Indian Pangolin is similar in habit to that of the Chinese Pangolin. The young appear to be produced at different times of the year. In peninsular India the young ones are reported during January, March and July. A single young is produced at birth, rarely two.

Status : Due to its nocturnal habit, its exact status is unknown. But, as with the Chinese Pangolin, the Indian Pangolin is also killed by man for its alleged medicinal value, hence its population has greatly reduced now.

Order Carnivora

WOLF

14. Canis lupus Linnaeus (E)

The wolf is about the size of an Alsation dog, and measures 90-105 cm in the head and body length and 67-75 cm in height at the shoulder. Its tail is less than half the length of head and body, and tipped black. The large skull, long powerful jaws, arching brows and the elevated forehead are characteristics of this animal. The dorsal colour of its body is greyish fulvous, usually with a brownish tinge, but sometimes mixed with black. Even reddish or rufous individuals are not unknown. Its face and the limbs are reddish and the lower surface is dingy white.

Distribution : In India, it occurs from the upper Himalaya to the desert zone, and dry open country in the Peninsular India. Extralimitally, it is found in Europe, southwestern, central and northern Asia, and North America.

Habits and habitat : The wolf lives in small packs in rocky hills or in dry open country around human habitation. Crevices in rocks, burrows in the sand dunes, caves, etc., provide it shelter. It hunts during night and animals such as antelope, fox, hare, rodent, etc., form its main prey items, but it does not spare a sheep or a goat, when within easy reach. Incidence of its lifting children is also known. It breeds mostly at the end of the rains and young ones, three to eight, are born about December. At high altitudes, however, it breeds later and pups are born in the spring.

Status : The wolf is much rarer now than it was sometimes back. The tendency of killing wolves by man exists in many parts of India for its alleged habit of lifting livestock and human babies. However, its surviving population is reported from Karnataka, Maharashtra, Gujarat, Rajasthan and Bihar. The latest census made in the Rann of Kutch gave its population to be around five dozens.

wolf

JACKAL

15. Canis aureus Linnaeus (V)

The jackal is among the most familiar animals of the country. It is closely related to the wolf, but lacks the elevated forehead and the arching brows.It is smaller than a village dog and possesses a bushy tail.It measures 60-80 cm in the length of head and body and 38-45 cm in height at the shoulder. Its coat colour is variable but is generally with a mixture of black and white, washed with buff about the shoulders, ears and legs; its head is light brown.

Distribution : This species occurs throughout India. Extralimitally, it is found in southeastern Europe, southwestern Asia and extends eastwards up to Thailand.

Habits and habitat : The jackal is adapted to live in every environment. It has been found at a height of 3660 m in the Himalaya, and is well-established around hill stations, but is commonly seen around villages in the plains. Its long-drawn, high pitched, morning and evening howl, repeated three to four times, is familiar to all. It is nocturnal in habit and comes out at dusk and retires at dawn. Its food consists of carrion, animals, birds and even fruits. It raids melon patches and sugarcane fields. It also preys on domestic animals and the poultry. It breeds throughout the year and the period of gestation is about 63 days. The number of young per litter is usually four.

jackal

Status : The population of the Jackal, which was once a very common animal, has greatly run down in many parts of India, due to its persecution for pelt. It is also killed for its habit of raiding melon and sugarcane fields. Further, extensive use of pesticides in agricultural fields has also affected its population.

RED FOX

16. *Vulpes vulpes* (Linnaeus)   (V)

The Red fox, as its name signifies, is reddish in colour. It has long, silky fur and a white-tipped, fluffy tail. It measures 50-70 cm in the head and body length and 35-45 cm in the length of tail. Its face is rufous in colour, with a dark spot below each eye. The backside of its ear is black at the tip. Its coat is luxurious in winter and the colour varies from red to grey.

Distribution : In India, this species occurs in the northwestern arid region and in the Himalaya from Kashmir to Sikkim. Extralimitally, it is found

red fox

in the greater part of the north and west of the Northern Hemisphere, including the Arctic.

Habits and habitat : This fox is an animal of dry, arid and semi-arid regions and inhabits sandy wastes, sand dunes and river beds with scattered bushes. In the Himalaya, however, it is found in the birchwood and near cultivations. It is nocturnal in habit and feeds on birds and small mammals; also picks up scraps of discarded food and offal near human habitation. Its breeding time is about the end of winter. The young ones, usually five to seven, are produced in March-April.

Status : The population of the Red Fox has greatly run down due to indiscriminate hunting and trapping for its handsome winter pelt.

INDIAN FOX

17. **Vulpes bengalensis** (Shaw)   (V)

The Indian Fox is a grey-coloured animal, having slender limbs, a black-tipped tail and the back of its ears of the same tone as the head and nape, but never black. It is slightly smaller and slimmer than the Red Fox, being 45-60 cm in the head and body length and 25-35 cm in the length of tail.

indian fox

Distribution : This fox is indigenous to India and occurs throughout the country, except in the extreme northwestern borders.

Habits and habitat : It lives in scrubs in flat and rocky areas, avoiding forests, and is common near cultivations. All day long it sleeps inside the self-dug burrow, but at night comes out singly or in pairs. It is a very clever creature and is amazingly quick on its feet. It feeds on termites, crabs, reptiles, field rats, etc.,and also on fruits specially of *ber*. It breeds between November and January, and the young, generally four in number, are born during February-April.

Status : The Indian Fox keeps a check on agricultural pests, and yet this pretty creature is hunted for its pelt, and also for its flesh and bones out of superstitious belief. Its population has depleted in many parts of the country due to the harmful effect of pesticides applied to crops in the field.

INDIAN WILD DOG

18. Cuon alpinus (Pallas) (V)

The Indian Wild Dog is midway between an wolf and a jackal in size, measuring from 90 to 96 cm in the head and body length and 36 to 43 cm in the length of tail, but differs from both of them in having six molar teeth in the lower jaw instead of seven. It has a red coat, short and powerful jaws, rounded ears, short legs and a black-tipped bushy tail. The red coat is distinctive, but varies from paler to deeper red, depending on the locality.

indian wild dog

Distribution : It occurs throughout India from the high altitudes of the Himalaya to the plains. Extralimitally, found in central and eastern Asia from Manchuria to Malay Peninsula.

Habits and habitat : It lives in forests and hunts in a pack, numbering 2 to 30 individuals, and usually preys upon Sambar, Chital, Musk Deer, pig, wild sheep, goat, antelope and the like. The wild dog has been known to kill bears, leopards and even tigers. Its breeding season is during winter, and four to six cups are produced at a time.

Status : The population of the Wild Dog in India has considerably depleted due to its continued persecution, and shrinkage of forest which in turn has diminished its prey species. Its number, as estimated recently, is about 80 in Palamau (Bihar), 54 in Kanha National Park (Madhya Pradesh) and 149 in Bandipur (Karnataka).

HIMALAYAN BROWN BEAR

19. Ursus arctos isabellinus Horsfield   (E)

The Himalayan Brown Bear is one of the subspecies of the Brown Bear of Europe and northern Asia. It is smaller in size, the male is about 170 cm in total length. It is heavier than the Himalayan Black Bear, and has a brown coat. Fur, in winter, is thick and shaggy, with underwool, and during summer it is shorter, thinner and darker. The colour varies in various shades of brown, ranging from very pale to dark and even to reddish brown, depending on the season. Some animals are silvery grey with white tip to the fur. A white half-collar on the chest is usually present.

Distribution : This subspecies occurs at higher elevations of the northwestern and central Himalaya. Extralimitally, It is known from Afghanistan, northwestern Pakistan, Pamirs, Tien Shan and Bhutan.

Habits and habitat : It inhabits chiefly the grass slopes above the tree line close to the snow. In winter, it hibernates or remains in torpid condition until the spring, when it may be seen on the hill sides. It enjoys a wide variety of food like young sprouts of grass, backwheat, berries, wild fruits, insects, various species of rats, etc., and at times takes larger animals. It mates in early summer, and the cubs, usually two, are born within the snug winter retreat.

Status : The population of the Himalayan Brown Bear has greatly depleted in recent years due to human interference in the Indian range of its occurrence. It is now rarely seen in inaccessible parts of the Himalaya and is an endangered species within our limits.

brown bear

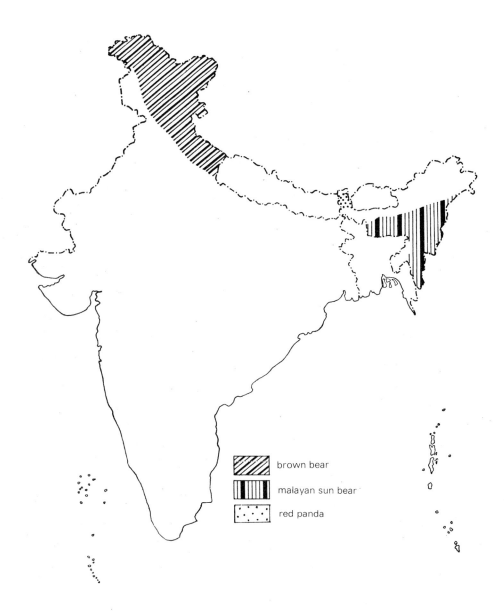

brown bear

malayan sun bear

red panda

47

MALAYAN SUN BEAR

20 Helarctos malayanus (Raffles) (R)

The Malayan Sun Bear is a small bear having short and coarse coat and measures 100-120 cm in the head and body length. The muzzle and the ears of this animal are short, and its claws are well-developed, pale or dusky in colour. The body-colour is chocolate brown or blackish; the muzzle and the chin is pale. A crescentic patch, often white, yellow or orange in colour, is present on its chest.

Distribution : In India, this bear occurs in the hilly terrain of northeastern India, south of the Brahmaputra river. Extralimitally, it is found in the eastern hill ranges of Bangladesh, Burma, southern China and as far southeast as Malaysia and Indonesia.

Habits and habitat : The Malayan Sun Bear inhabits hilly forests. It is nocturnal in habit and is a good climber. It is essentially frugivorous and prefers honey; like other bears, it also takes insects and feeds on animals and birds. Said to be monogamous, it mates between May and June and the young ones are born about September.

Status : Within the Indian limits, this bear is seldom reported and appears to be rare.

malayan sun bear

48

SLOTH BEAR

21. Melursus ursinus (Shaw)   (V)

The Sloth Bear is almost as big as a Himalayan Black Bear but is slim, and measures 140-160 cm in the head and body length. Its body is covered all over with long, coarse, shaggy black hair, with a V-shaped white mark on the chest. Its head is broad between the ears, and the muzzle long, giving the face a triangular appearance. The legs are bowed, the feet flat and the pug-marks are strangely human-like. The claws on the forefeet are strong and whitish.

Distribution : This bear is found all over India from the Himalayan foot-hills to the extreme southernmost parts. It is also found in Sri Lanka.

Habits and Habitat : It inhabits rocky, forested hills close to water; sleeps during the day in a cave or in some safe retreat and forages throughout the night. It eats fruits, flowers, tubers honey, various kinds of insects especially white-ants, grubs and the like. The Sloth Bear has strong liking for the fleshy petalled flowers of Mahua *(Madhuka latifolia)*. It also climbs the palm trees and drinks up the toddy from the toddy-pots. Instances of robbing birds' nests and eating eggs are also known. At times it also raids crops. It mates during the summer and the young ones, usually two in number, are born in December-January.

Status : The Sloth Bear has disappeared from many places where it was very common one or two generations ago. The reasons of its decline are the destruction of its habitat for human use, and was killed in the past for its bile which was used in medicine and trapped for keeping in Zoos or for entertainment.

sloth bear

RED PANDA

22. **Ailurus fulgens** F. Cuvier (R)

The Red Panda is a handsome animal having a rounded head, large pointed ears, stumpy muzzle and hairy soled legs with retractile claws as in the cats. Its head and body length measures 55-60 cm and the length of the tail 35-40 cm or so. Its dense woolly coat is bright chestnut and the fluffy tail is ringed with light and dark shades of rusty red, the tip being black. The underside and the legs are black. The face and the lower lip are white, with a vertical red stripe from the eye to the gape. The ears are dark red on the outer surface, but white near the edges and inside.

Distribution : It is found in the Himalaya from Nepal and Sikkim to Upper Burma and southern China.

Habits and habitat : The Red Panda inhabits temperate forest at altitudes ranging from 1500 to 3500 m. It lives usually in pairs. It is arboreal and occupies hollows of trees, fork between two branches and rock crevices. It is mainly nocturnal, but is also active during early morning and before sunset. Vegetable matters like sprouts of bamboo, fruits, roots, etc. are the most favourite food items of the Red Panda. It also takes insects and steals eggs and chicks from birds' nests. The young, two in number, are born in the spring.

red panda

Status : The Red Panda is very rare within the Indian limits, due to shrinkage of its habitat. Moreover, it is being trapped and hunted for its charming pelt. A few decades ago it was fairly known in the Darjeeling district of West Bengal. At present it has almost vanished from this area, except sporadically occurring in the Neora Valley in Kalimpong Forest Division and on the eastern slope of the Singalila Ridge. However, in recent surveys by the Zoological Survey of India parties it has been observed in Singhik, Chunthang, Menshithang, Lachen, Yaksam and Lachung areas of Sikkim.

ERMINE OR STOAT

23.   **Mustela erminea** Linnaeus   (R)

The body of the Stoat is slender, measuring about 20-25 cm from tip of the snout to the base of tail; the latter being half of that. Its sole is covered with hair except over the toe-pads. Its fur is soft, with woolly underfur. The summer coat is chestnut or reddish brown above and white below. The winter coat is entirely white except the tail-tip, which remains black. Its fore- and hind paws are white contrasting with the legs.

Distribution : A Palaearctic species, occurs in India in Kashmir only.

Habits and habitat : The Ermine lives in holes in the ground, amongst rocks and heaps of stone or in hollows of trees. It is usually nocturnal, but hunts during the day time also. It kills any animal it can master, but feeds mainly on rodents. It also preys on hares and game birds. A very active climber, it plunders eggs and nestlings from birds' nests. It mates in March and five to eight young ones are born in April or May.

Status : The Ermine has always been rare within the Indian limits. In Europe and other Asian countries. Its population has depleted due to over-exploitation for its fur.

ermine

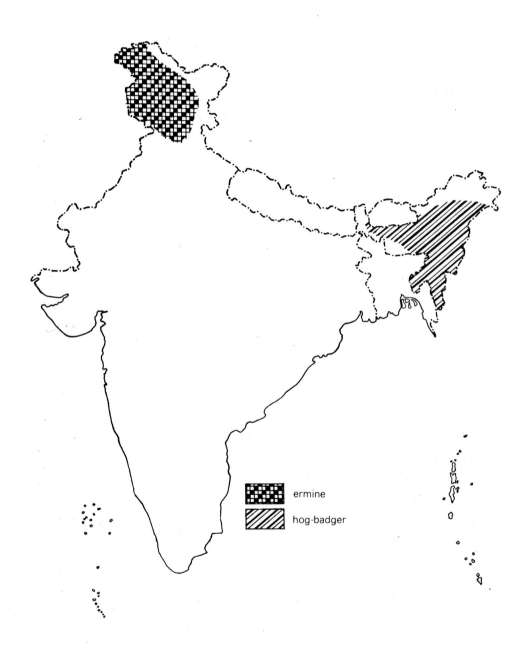

ermine

hog-badger

52

RATEL OR HONEY BADGER

24. **Mellivora capensis** (Schreber)   (V)

The Ratel has a squat body, short and stumpy legs, strong large claws and a small tail. Unlike Hog-Badger its snout is not projecting. It is 75-90 cm long inclusive of a short tail of 15-18 cm or so. it is tawny-white or grey above and black below, a most unusual colour-pattern amongst mammals. The undersurface of tail is deep black.

Distribution : In India the Ratel occurs from the base of the Himalaya to Cape Comorin, with the exception of Malabar Coast, southern part of West Bengal and the countries east of the Bay of Bengal. Extralimitally, it is known from southwestern Asia and Africa.

honey badger

Habits and habitat : It inhabits desert and dry deciduous forest. Prefers hilly broken country and the banks of streams. It resembles bears in its habit of digging holes on the riverside, probably in search of water. Ratel though omnivorous, is essentially a flesh-eater and feeds on mammals, birds, reptiles, insects, etc., but also likes fruit and honey. It is destructive to livestock too. Its hide is thick and possesses large stink glands to defend against enemies. Nothing much is known about the breeding habit. The period of gestation is about six months and two young ones are born at a time.

Status : The population of the Ratel in India has depleted greatly in the last few decades. The animal is being killed as it is destructive to man's domestic stock.

HOG-BADGER

25. *Arctonyx collaris* F. Cuvier (I)

The Hog-Badger has a long but truncated snout, with terminal disc containing the nostrils much like that of a pig. Its broad squat body and stumpy legs resemble those of a bear and long powerful digging claws those

hog-badger

54

of a badger. Ears are short and rounded. The length of the head and body varies between 55 and 65 cm and the tail about one-fourth of it. The dorsal colour is a mixture of black, white and buff, which gives the coat a greyish tone. The underside and the limbs are dusky. The head is whitish with a dark brown band extending from the upper lip to around the eye and ear and another dusky stripe across the cheek. The throat, sides of the neck and the tail are whitish. The pale throat and the dark stripe on the cheek distinguish it from the true Badger.

Distribution : It occurs in northeastern India. Extralimitally, it is found in Tibet and southeastern Asia as far east as Malaysia.

Habits and habitat : In India, the Hog-Badger inhabits tropical forests and prefers rocky, broken terrain having crevices and fissures, for shelter. It is a very bold animal and uses its teeth and claws during encounters. The nauseous discharge of its stink glands is, however, very repulsive to its enemies. In its feeding habit, it is omnivorous. Nothing has been recorded of the breeding habits.

Status : It appears to have colonized in eastern India in recent times, and is rarely seen. Its exact status is unknown.

MALABAR CIVET

26. Viverra megaspila Blyth (E)

The Malabar Civet is apparently similar to the Large Indian Civet in size. Its head and body measures 75-80 cm in length and the tail 32-35 cm. It is distinguished by its naked sole with interdigital webs, and in having a crest of black erectile hair on the back from shoulder to the whole length of the tail. The latter possesses six broad, black rings, with incomplete yellowish white rings between them. The ground colour of its body is yellowish, the hinder portion being marked with large black spots instead of stripes. Its head is grey, the chin brown and the base of the ears a little darker. The neck is white in front, dusky on the back and has two or three black gorgets on the sides.

Distribution : Within the Indian limits it occurs in the coastal districts of Kerala.

Habits and habitat : The Malabar Civet mainly inhabits the richly wooded plains, but is occasionally found on the elevated forest-tracts. Its feeding habit is very similar to that of the Large Indian Civet and is very destructive to poultry.

binturong

malabar civet

Status : In the last century, this civet was quite a common animal in Travancore. From the beginning of this century, however, it has hardly been reported. The species appears to be greatly endangered, probably nearing extinction, and needs conservation on priority basis.

malabar civet

SPOTTED LINSANG

27. **Prionodon pardicolor** Hodgson (V)

The Spotted Linsang is a beautiful looking member of the civet family, with elongated body, pointed muzzle and short limbs. Its tail possesses eight to ten dark rings, separated by an equal number of pale rings. It measures 37-40 cm in the head and body length and the tail is slightly smaller. The rich orange or fulvous colour of the body with large black spots arranged in longitudinal rows distinguish it from other civets.

spotted linsang

Distribution : This species occurs in the central and eastern Himalaya, and also in northern Burma and southern China.

Habits and habitat : It inhabits hill forests at elevations between 150 and 1850 m or above. It is not gregarious and is equally at home on trees and on the ground. It preys chiefly on insects, small birds and small mammals. It breeds twice in a year, once in February and again in August, in the hollows of decayed trees and two young ones are produced in each litter.

Status : This beautiful civet is nowhere common due to shrinkage of its habitat and for being hunted for its graceful pelt.

spotted linsang

BINTURONG

28. Arctictis binturong (Raffles) (I)

The Binturong is distinguished from other members of the civet family, by its bear-like long, shaggy coat. It measures 75-90 cm in the length of head and body. Its tail is as long as the body and is thick at the base and clothed with long bristly hair. The body colour of this animal is black, grizzled with white or buff, giving it a greyish look.

Distribution : In the Indian region, this species is known to occur from Nepal to northeastern India. Extralimitally, it occurs from Burma to Malaysia and Indonesia.

Habits and habitat : The Binturong inhabits dense, tropical foot-hill forest and higher up in the temperate region up to 2000 m or so. It is nocturnal and arboreal and prefers hollows of trees for shelter during the day. It feeds from dusk to dawn on small mammals, birds, fishes, earthworms and insects. It also takes fruits. Nothing is known of its breeding habits.

Status : Because of its secretive nocturnal mode of life, the Binturong is rarely seen. Hence, nothing is known about its exact status. However, the population has depleted considerably and is very rarely reported now a days. Three specimens were observed in 1982 in Menshithang and Hee Gyathan Reserve Forests in north Sikkim by the Zoological Survey of India party.

binturong

CRABEATING MONGOOSE

29. Herpestes urva (Hodgson) (V)

The Crabeating Mongoose is large, being 45-57 cm in the head and body length and 30-35 cm in the length of tail. It is characterized by the presence of a white stripe running from the angle of the mouth to the side of the neck. Its hair are coarse, dusky iron grey in colour, with white tips. The head, hands and the feet of this mongoose are dark brown or black.

Distribution : This species occurs at low elevations and in foothills from Nepal to eastern India, thence eastwards it extends to Burma, southern China and the northern portion of Malay Peninsula.

Habits and habitat : Like other mongooses, it lives in holes in the ground. Unlike other species, however, it is more aquatic in habit and fearlessly enters hill streams to hunt for snails, crabs, fishes and frogs. It squirts out a fetid fluid from its large anal glands, which acts as a means of defence. Nothing is known about its breeding habits.

Status : Vulnerable. This mongoose is not commonly noticed in the area of its occurrence where it was once well known. Habitat destruction for human use appears to be the primary factor for the reduction of its number.

crabeating mongoose

crabeating mungoose

STRIPED HYENA

30. Hyaena hyaena (Linnaeus) (V)

The Striped Hyena is a digitigrade animal, with strong, blunt nonretractile and slightly curved claws. The head and fore-body are massive and the limbs rather long. A thick crest of long hair is present on its neck and back. The head and body length of this animal measures 90-110 cm and the tail 25-35 cm or so. Its coat-colour varies from dirty grey to cream buff, with blackish transverse stripes on the body and limbs.

Distribution : This species is widely distributed throughout India, but is found in small numbers in suitable pockets. It has not been recorded from the countries east of the Bay of Bengal. Extralimitally, it occurs in southwestern Asia and northern Africa.

Habits and habitat : It is solitary in habit and is generally seen in scrub, dry open jungles or in low hills and ravines where convenient holes and caves are available for shelter. It is nocturnal and rambles between sunset and sunrise. Its principal food consists of the carcasses of animals that have died of disease or been killed by beasts of prey, and very often it carries off portions of the body of food-animal to its den. Also, it shares the coarser remains of refused food of other predators. It mates in winter and the young ones, probably three or four in number, are born during the summer.

Status : Its number has greatly depleted at present, due to habitat destruction and persecution by man for its alleged habit of lifting livestock and human babies. Its population size in the Gir Forest, Gujarat, as estimated recently, is about 84 individuals.

striped hyena

JUNGLE CAT

31. Felis chaus Güldenstaedt (V)

The Jungle Cat is a medium-sized cat, with long legs and a short tail. It measures 56-94 cm in the head and body length and 20-31 cm in the length of tail. Its coat is harsh in summer but soft in winter. The colour varies from yellowish grey to tawny rufous and the undersurface is paler. The pattern on the sides of the body is absent, however, vestiges of stripes are present on the neck and the chest. The limbs are often marked with transverse bars. The backside of ears are reddish with a pale central spot, ending in a small pencil of black hair. The tail is black at the tip and has a few black rings near the distal end.

Distribution : The Jungle Cat has a very wide range of occurrence from northern parts of Africa to southeastern Asia. In India, however, it is found from the Himalaya to Cape Comorin.

Habits and habitat : It prefers bushy jungles, scrubs and forests, also frequents cornfield, sugarcane and long grass fields. It is nocturnal in habit and preys upon small animals of all kinds. At times, it enters the outskirts of villages to raid on poultry. Instances of its feeding on fish and crab are also known. It perhaps breeds twice in a year and two to four young ones are born in each litter.

Status : This Cat is not so commonly seen in India now a days than it was before. The main reason of its decline is the shrinkage of its habitat. It is also being killed by man for its habit of raiding on poultry as also for its pelt.

jungle cat

INDIAN DESERT CAT

32.   Felis silvestris ornata Gray   (V)

The Indian Desert Cat is of the size of a domestic cat, with a long tail. It measures 45-60 cm in the head and body length and the tail is about half of that. The latter is tapering, and the terminal half of it is ringed with black. A pair of cheek stripes and a number of dark transverse lines are present on the outer side of the limbs. Its coat-colour is sandy to pale yellowish, infused with grey and marked with numerous small black spots. The undersurface is pale rufescent, with a few dark spots; the chin, the throat and the front of the breast are white. The ears are coloured like the back and have a few brown hair at the tips.

indian desert cat

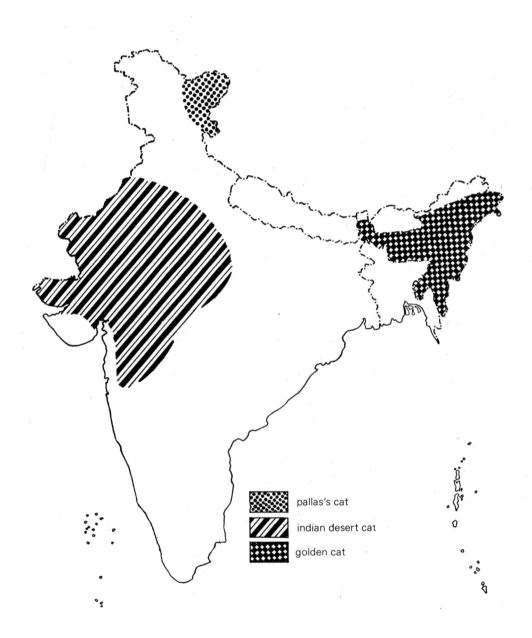

pallas's cat

indian desert cat

golden cat

Distribution : This cat is found all over Rajasthan, Kutch (Gujarat) and parts of central India. It has also been reported from Pune (Maharashtra) by Lamba (1967). Extralimitally, it is known from Pakistan.

Habits and habitat : It inhabits the scrub jungle in arid areas, and its principal food is rodents and birds. Its breeding habit is unknown.

Status : In earlier days, the Desert Cat was commonly seen in Rajasthan and Gujarat, but has now become very scarce. It is ruthlessly killed for its beautiful pelt. Its status is at present vulnerable.

PALLAS'S CAT

33.   *Felis manul* Pallas   (I)

The Pallas's Cat is a small cat with a broad head, low set ears and a thick cylindrical tail. It measures 45-60 cm in the head and body length and 20-30 cm in the length of tail. The ears are short and widely separated; its backside is buff with a black tip. The fur on the body is soft and thick, having a silvery grey to yellowish buff hue; thoracic portion is rather brown. Some faint black stripes are present on the sides. Head is broad with scattered

pallas's cat

black spots above and a pair of cheek stripes. The fore-and hind limbs have traces of dark transverse stripes. The tail is thick and bushy with a broad black terminal tuft, preceded by four to six narrow black rings.

Distribution : Within the Indian limits this cat is known only from Ladakh in Jammu and Kashmir. Extralimitally, it occurs in Iran, Pakistan, Tibet and Central Asia up to southern Siberia.

Habits and habitat : Nothing is definitely known about this cat, except that it lives among rocks, and preys on small animals and birds.

Status : The status of the Indian population of the Pallas's Cat is unknown; elsewhere too it is rarely seen. It is being killed for its furry skin.

GOLDEN CAT

34. **Felis temmincki** Vigors & Horsfield   (R)

The Golden Cat is the largest of the smaller oriental cats and measures 75-105 cm in the head and body length and 45-56 cm in the length of tail. The colour of its body varies from golden brown to dark brown or

golden cat

ochreous tawny or grey, and without any pattern over it. The undersurface and the inner side of legs are buff or white; faint stripes are, however, present on the nape, throat and inner side of foreleg. The face markings give the animal a striking appearance. Most conspicuous is a horizontal white cheek stripe, edged with black, running below the eye to behind the gape. In addition, there are conspicuous white stripes also on the inner side and along the lower margin of the eye. The tail is between one-half and two-thirds of the head and body length, with the upperside of the tip slightly darker.

Distribution : This species occurs from Sikkim to eastern India. Extralimitally, it is found in Nepal, Bhutan, Bangladesh, from Burma to Vietnam and southern China.

Habits and habitat : The Golden Cat inhabits dense forests in the Terai and Duars and in the tropical rain forests; also ascends temperate zone up to an altitude of about 1500 m. It takes shelter among rocks, crevices of boulders and on trees. It preys on sheep, goats and birds, in absence of which takes to livestock and poultry. Very stout and bold, it even knocks down much larger animals than itself. It gives birth to two young ones in each litter.

Status : This cat is rarely seen. The depletion in its population has occurred, mainly due to the cutting down of primary forests in the range of its occurrence for human need, and occasional persecution by man for economic purposes.

LEOPARD-CAT

35. Felis bengalensis Kerr   (V)

The colour and markings of this cat give it the appearance of a miniature Leopard, hence its name the Leopard-Cat. Its size is that of a domestic cat but is rather long in the legs, measures 60-66 cm in the head and body length and 28-30 cm in the length of tail. The colour of the body above is pale fulvous, varying from ochraceous to greyish and is ornamented throughout with numerous elongated black or rusty spots; the undersurface is white but spotted. There are two narrow black cheek stripes enclosing a white area between them, and four black stripes run over the head from the inner corner of the eyes. The stripes running from the forehead break up into elongate spots on the shoulders. The ears are rounded, with a large, white spot on the back of each. The tail approximates half the length of head and body and indistinctly ringed towards the tip. Transverse stripes are present on its forelegs.

eopard-cat

Distribution : It is found all over India ranging from the Himalaya to Cape Comorin. Extralimitally, it is known widely from many Asian countries, from eastern Siberia through Manchuria, Korea, China, Tibet, southeast to the Philippine Islands.

Habits and habitat : The Leopard-Cat inhabits forest areas far and near human habitations and usually takes shelter in the hollows of large trees. It is nocturnal and starts prowling from the evening. It preys generally on mammals and birds that it can manage to catch and is also very destructive to poultry. In southern India, it breeds about May and three to four young ones are born in each litter.

Status : The population of the Leopard-Cat has depleted in recent years, due to habitat destruction and its persecution by man for its habit of raiding poultry, as also for the beautiful pelt. It is often kept as a pet by private persons.

RUSTYSPOTTED CAT

36. **Felis rubiginosa** Geoffroy (R)

The Rustyspotted Cat is about half or three quarters of the size of a domestic cat, with a moderately long tail. The head and body length measures 35-48 cm and the tail is about half of that. Its coat is soft and smooth, of rufescent grey colour and patterned with brown bars and spots arranged in more lor less regular lines. The dark brown markings on the head and shoulders change to rusty on the flanks and are reduced to smaller round spots on the hind quarter. Four dark lines run from the eyes and the base of nose to over the head. A pair of cheek stripes are present. The belly and the inner side of legs are white, with large dark spots. The tail is uniformly coloured or at most with very indistinct pattern. The ears are small, rounded and rufous on the outer side, with a large pale spot.

Distribution : This cat is sporadically reported from Jammu, western, southern and central India. Extralimitally, it occurs in Sri Lanka.

Habits and habitat : It is less arboreal; inhabits scrub and grass jungles and is often found in forests in the vicinity of villages. Two or three kittens are born in a litter. However, hybrids between the Rustyspotted Cat and the domestic cat are not unknown.

Status : The population of the Rustyspotted Cat has always been found to be scarce. The species is known from a few specimens only.

rustyspotted cat

| ● | rustyspotted cat |
| ▨ | fishing cat |

FISHING CAT

37. *Felis viverrina* Bennett (V)

The Fishing Cat is a medium-sized, stockily built animal, with elongate head, short legs and a short tail. It measures 70-86 cm in the head and body length and 25-33 cm in the length of tail. The ears are short and blunt, their outer side is black with a white spot. The forefeet are provided with moderately developed interdigital webs. The tail is less than half of head and body in length. It is marked with incomplete dark rings and has a black tip. Its coat is short and coarse, and is coloured tawny grey to brownish mouse-grey. Six to eight black lines run down the forehead to the neck. A pair of cheek stripes is also present. The body markings consist of elongate spots arranged in longitudinal rows.

Distribution : It is found in suitable pockets throughout India and is reported from Assam, Sunderbans (West Bangal), Chilka Lake (Orissa), and the backwaters of Kerala. Extralimitally, it occurs in Sri Lanka, Pakistan, Nepal, Bhutan, Bangladesh, from Burma to Vietnam, Malaysia, Indonesia and southern China.

Habits and habitat : The Fishing Cat inhabits scrub and thick forests, and frequents tidal creeks, rivers, mangrove swamps, hill streams and reed

fishing cat

beds. It feeds on small animals, birds, molluscs and fishes which it flips out of water with its paws. It has also been known to attack animals like goats and young calves. Nothing exactly is known about its breeding habits, but a female with two young ones has been seen in April.

Status : The population of this cat has depleted due to loss of its habitat for various reasons and is now known from a few pockets only. It is rare in Sri Lanka too.

MARBLED CAT

38.   Felis marmorata charltoni Gray   (V)

The Marbled Cat appears to be a miniature Clouded Leopard. It is slightly larger than a domestic cat and has an extremely long and bushy tail.

marbled cat

The head and body length measures 45-60 cm and the tail 35-54 cm. Its outer coat has many large irregular blotches arranged more or less longitudinally giving it a marbling pattern. Its head is short and broad and is marked with one black stripe running up from the upper margin of each eye, two black stripes on the cheek and small spots on the forehead. The ground colour varies from brownish grey to bright ochre or rufous brown and is ventrally paler. The heavily spotted legs and the tail are of the same rich hue as the body.

Distribution : This cat is reported from Sikkim, West Bengal (Darjeeling) and Nagaland in India, but very likely occurs in the whole of northeastern India in suitable localities. It is also found in Nepal, Bhutan, Bangladesh, Burma, Thailand, Malaysia, Vietnam and Indonesia.

Habits and habitat : It prefers thick forests, mostly in colder climates. It is arboreal and nocturnal in habits and feeds on birds and small mammals.

Status : The Marbled Cat is seldom seen mainly because of its nocturnal and arboreal habits. It is believed to be very rare. The decline in the population has been due to shrinkage of its habitat and as it is being killed for its charming pelt.

LYNX

39. Felis lynx isabellina Blyth (R)

The Lynx, a strongly built animal, high on the legs, is distinguished from other cats in having a long tuft of hair on the tip of the ears. It measures 85-90 cm in the head and body length. The hair on the cheeks are lengthened behind to form a ruff on the face. The colour of the body varies from pale slaty grey to isabelline, occasionally with faint spots on the flanks and limbs. The tail is short, terminally black and less than a quarter of the head and body length.

Distribution : Within the Indian limits, it occurs in Gilgit and Ladakh (Jammu and Kashmir). Extralimitally, it is known from Tibet to as far north as Tienshan and Altai Mountains.

Habits and habitat : The Lynx inhabits dense cover of willow, reeds, tall grasses and scrubs at altitudes between 2700 and 3400 m during the summer. In winter, however, it decends even up to 1525 m. It is an excellant climber, and well known for its keen eye-sight and hearing. The Lynx is extremely blood-thirsty and savage, and preys on birds and mammals, often on sheep and goats. It breeds probably in August, and two to three young ones are born in each litter.

lynx

CARACAL

40. Felis caracal schmitzi Matschie   (E)

The Caracal is a medium-sized cat, having long legs and a short tail. It measures 60-80 cm in the head and body length and 23-32 cm in the length of tail. A dark spot on each side of the upper lip and two short vertical bars above the eyes are present. Ears, set fairly close together, are triangular and pointed, with a long erect tuft of black hairs at the tip; backside of the ears are black. Its coat is short on the back, but comparatively woolly on the belly; uniformly reddish sandy grey above, fading to buff or white below. It has no trace of any pattern except for some faint spots on the undersurface. The tail and the slender limbs are of the same colour as the body; the tail tip is not black.

Distribution : It is found in the central and northwestern India, and through Pakistan westwards to Arabia.

Habits and habitat : The Caracal inhabits the arid and semiarid areas; generally found among bushes, grass, scattered forests, low scrubby hillocks and sandy country. The hollows of trees, crevices among rocks and boulders are its common shelter during the day. It is nocturnal and hunts from dusk to dawn. It preys on small birds and mammals but sometimes knocks down even larger animals like antelope. The number of young per brood varies between two and four.

Status : The Caracal was a rare animal fifty years ago. It has become rarer now and is endangered, mainly due to loss of its preferred habitat and hunting of the animal for its pelt.

caracal

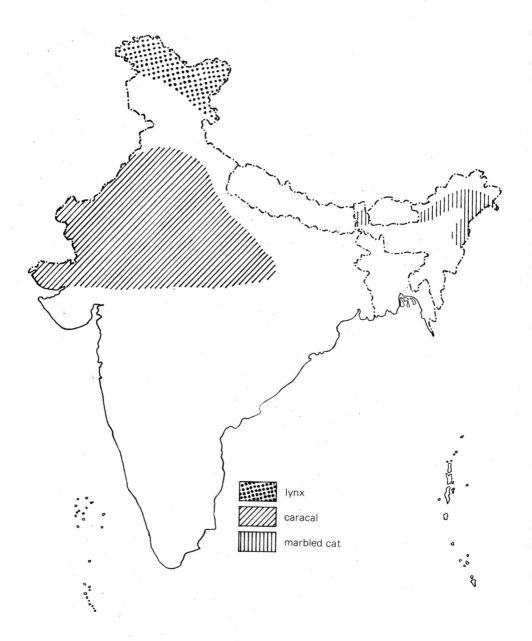

lynx

caracal

marbled cat

CLOUDED LEOPARD

41. Neofelis nebulosa (Griffith) (R)

The Clouded Leopard has a long body and tail. It measures about 95-120 cm in the head and body length and 75-86 cm in the length of tail. Darker trapezoidal or irregular rosettes are present on its body, which at places are edged with black. The general colour of the body varies from grey to earthy brown. Head is spotted and its face is marked with cheek stripes. The limbs and the underparts are marked with large black or tawny spots. The tail has dusky rings, often interrupted at the sides; the rings near the body are traversed by a longitudinal band. Ears are rounded and black, relieved by a greyish patch in the centre.

clouded leopard

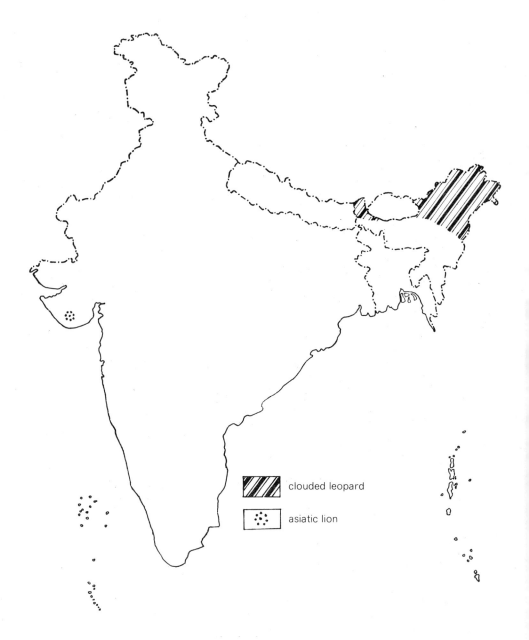

clouded leopard

asiatic lion

Distribution : The Clouded Leopard occurs in India from Sikkim to Arunachal Pradesh, Nagaland and the eastern portion of Assam. Extralimitally, it is found in eastern Nepal, Burma, southern China, Malaysia and Indonesia.

Habits and habitat : This species inhabits mostly the dense evergreen and the sub-Himalayan tropical forests. It is arboreal and nocturnal in habits and preys upon small or large mammals and birds. It sometimes visits villages in hilly terrain and in the tea garden areas of northern Bengal to lift domestic pigs and goats.

Status : It is rarely seen due to its nocturnal and arboreal habits. However, it is being killed for its beautiful pelt for economic purpose and has also suffered depletion in population due to the loss of habitat.

LEOPARD OR PANTHER

42. **Panthera pardus** (Linnaeus)   (V)

The Panther or the Leopard, as it is called, is much smaller than a tiger even when fully adult, being 170 to 215 cm in total length, including the tail, and about 60 cm in shoulder-height. Its coat is sleek and short-haired. The

leopard

ground colour is highly variable from pale yellow, warm grey, rich tawny to rufous fawn, and has dark spots arranged in rosettes all over the sides of the body and the tail, except at the tip which is ringed. The spots, down the middle of the back and on the head, limbs and belly are solid black instead of being arranged in rosettes. Melanistic or black panthers are also known.

Distribution : The Leopard occurs throughout Africa and Asia, with the exception of the high Tibetan plateau and Siberia. In India, however, it is found all over the country.

Habits and habitat : It inhabits a variety of habitats like the hills, plains, thick forests and scrub jungles, away from and near human habitations. It is an excellent climber, and graceful and agile in its movements. Though medium sized, it is very strong, and may kill even large-sized animals like cows and bullocks. In forests, it lives on deer, pig, antelope, hare, monkey, rat, peafowl, and on quite a large number of small birds. It often lifts goats, dogs, etc. from villages. It breeds throughout the year and the gestation period varies between 84 and 98 days. Two to four cubs are produced in each litter.

Status : The population of the Leopard has run down to a vulnerable state within the last few decades, due to excessive hunting for its graceful pelt, reduction of its prey species, habitat shrinkage, etc.

TIGER
43. **Panthera tigris** (Linnaeus)   (V)

The graceful built of a tiger is well known. The rich reddish yellow to orange rufous coat marked with black stripes and the black-ringed tail are characteristic of this animal. Ventrally, it is white. The ears are black on the outer side, each with a prominent white spot. It measures about 260-290 cm in total length including the tail.

Distribution : The tiger occurs in many parts of Asia, but it is better known from India, where it is found practically throughout the country, from Himalaya to Cape Comorin except the northwestern region.

Habits and habitat : The tiger lives in varied habitats like dry open jungles, humid evergreen forests and mangrove swamps. It is endowed with good swimming power. It hunts between sunset and dawn and covers long distances in the course of a night's haunting. It is enormously powerful and all kinds of animals fall victim of its prey. It may eat even fowl, fish, reptiles, etc. In the absence of natural prey, it may take to cattle-lifting. It mates after

tiger

rains, and the young ones, usually two to six, are born between February and May. The cubs are looked after by the female till they are capable of killing their own prey.

Status : In the last century, the tiger was very common in India. It has now reached to a vulnerable state. The main reason of its decline in number is the uncontrolled felling of trees which has resulted in the shrinkage of its cover and decrease of its prey species. Further, it was killed in the past for its magnificent skin. It is estimated that in India, there were about 40,000 tigers half a century ago but the number gradually decreased to less than two thousand in 1972. However, a number of sanctuaries established under collaborative 'Project Tiger' by the Government of India and the World Wildlife Fund, for the care and maintenance of this animal, paid dividend, and its number rose to 757 in Tiger Reserves and 3115 in the whole country in 1979.

ASIATIC LION

44. Panthera leo persica (Meyer) (E)

The Asiatic Lion is a gracious looking animal, with a pale yellowish brown to sandy grey coat devoid of any marking. A light or dark coloured shaggy mane adorns the head in male. The tail has a long tassel of hair at the end. Cubs are marked with spots and stripes. Adult males measure 270-300 cm in total length, the females are a little smaller.

asiatic lion

Distribution : The lion is at present restricted to the Gir Forest in Gujarat, India.

Habits and habitat : The lion lives in family parties in dry, rugged, mixed deciduous forests predominated with stunted trees like babul, teak, palas, bamboo, etc., and an undergrowth of thorny bushes. It hunts by night and preys on antelope, deer, pig, cattle, etc. Usually it mates between October and November and two to three young ones are delivered in January-February, after a gestation period of about 116 days.

Status : This subspecies thrived well in the Middle East, Asia Minor, Arabia and greater parts of northern and central India as far south as Narbada river, in historic times. It was known in southwestern Rajasthan even in earlier part of this century. At present, with every possible and rigorous protection extended to it, it is fighting out its last battle for survival at the Gir Forest in Gujarat. As a result of effective protection and improvement in the habitat condition, its estimated population which was only 180 individuals in 1974 increased to 205 in 1979.

SNOW LEOPARD
45. Panthera uncia (Schreber) (R)

The Snow Leopard or the Ounce is like the Leopard in general appearance but is slightly smaller. Its head is squarish, with high forehead and vertical chin; measures from 190 to 220 cm in total length. The coat is beautiful, and the fur soft and thick. Paler spots grouped into rosettes are present all over the body and tail. The head, nape and lower part of the limbs possess solid spots. The colour, in general, is pale grey, sometimes with a little amount of rufous or buff. The ventral colour is white, occasionally with a few light spots. The ears are black, but each has a large yellowish spot.

Distribution : Within the Indian limits, the Snow Leopard is distributed in the Himalaya from Kashmir to Sikkim. Extralimitally, it is known from Bhutan, Pakistan, Tibet, central Asia and the Altais.

Habits and habitat : Generally the Ounce occurs on high altitudes ranging approximately from 3000 to 4000 m, but in winter visits lower

snow leopard

elevations up to 2000 m or so. It preys on ibex, markhor, tahr, marmots pikas, hares and birds; also lifts sheep, goats, and ponies from villages and hill slope pastures.

Status : The Ounce was once quite common throughout the Himalaya. From the last century it has been killed in great numbers for its esteemed skin for making costly dresses, gloves, cushions and other luxury items, so much so that its population has now dwindled to an alarming stage. Attempts have been made to protect it in Dachigam Sanctuary in Kashmir since 1951 and is also included in the list of protected animals of the Govt. of India since 1952. In order to conserve this beautiful animal, a ban on the trade of its fur has also been imposed by the International Fur Trade Federation in 1971 .

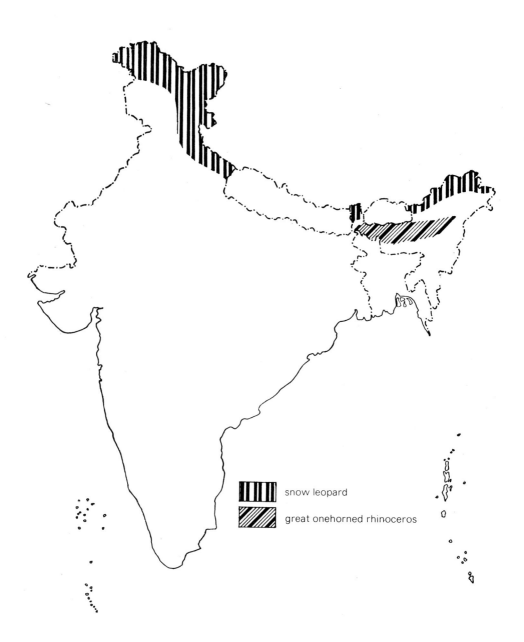

snow leopard

great onehorned rhinoceros

CHEETAH

46. Acinonyx jubatus venaticus (Griffith) (E)

The Cheetah is a little smaller than the Panther and much lighter in built, measures approximately 90 to 130 cm in the head and body length and 60 to 72 cm in the length of tail. It has a harsh coat; the colour varies from tawny-grey to ruddy fawn above, paler below, with solid, round black spots all over the body and the tail. A dark, black streak runs down the inner corner of each eye to the upper lip. Moreover, the cheetah has a narrow chest, long limbs, and partially retractile claws.

Distribution : The known distribution of the Cheetah is mainly Africa, and the dryer parts of southwestern Asia including India. However, it seems to be no more extant in India, and in all probabilities has also disappeared from other Asian countries.

Habits and habitat : The Cheetah lives in the rugged hill-dotted plains and arid areas. It is less nocturnal than most members of the cat family. So far known, it is the fastest animal on legs, and can achieve a terrific speed of 115-120 km an hour, within a distance of about 370 m, which is very useful to it in hunting the fleet-footed prey. Its favourite preys are blackbucks, gazelles, deer, hares and birds. The Cheetah is easily tamed and used for hunting purpose.

cheetah

Status : Once the Cheetah was quite common in India, but now we have lost it irretrievably through our imprudence. Possibly, the practice of taming adult cheetah and training it for hunting, and complete failure in its captive breeding, have greatly decreased its number from the last century. Moreover, shrinkage of its habitat, killing by man and high mortality rate among the cubs, contributed much towards its extermination from India. A few stray reports of its occurrence in southern India were available up to 1951 and 1952 but it has not been heard of since then.

Order Perissodactyla

GREAT ONEHORNED RHINOCEROS

47. **Rhinoceros unicornis** Linnaeus   (V)

The Great Onehorned Rhinoceros is the largest land mammal next to the elephant, and measures 300-315 cm in the head and body length and about 180 cm in the shoulder-height. Unlike the African rhino, its hide is hairless. The skin of the body is divided into large shields by heavy folds before and behind the shoulders, in front of the thighs and on the buttocks. The folds behind the shoulders and in front of the thighs are continuous

great onehorned rhinoceros

across the back and those in front of the shoulders are not continued right across the back. The skin is studded with convex tubercles on the shoulders, thighs and the buttocks. The colour of its body is blackish grey throughout. A single well-developed horn is present in both the sexes which measures 38-41 cm. The horn grows throughout life, and if lost is reproduced.

Distribution : Long back it used to occur extensively in the Indo-Gangetic plains and along the base of the Himalaya from Nepal to Assam. There is a record that the Great Moghul Emperor Baber hunted it even near Peshawar in Pakistan in 1526. At present, it is known from scattered areas of Nepal, northern West Bengal and Assam.

Habits and habitat : The Great Onehorned Rhinoceros is a denizen of the grass-jungles and prefers swampy ground. It is solitary in habit, though several individuals may sometimes occupy the same patch of jungle. It is a grazer and feeds mainly on grass. Its breeding rate is very slow; mating takes places between February and April, and the period of gestation varies from 12 to 19 months in different areas. The calf, usually a single is born around October.

Status : The population of the Great Onehorned Rhinoceros has greatly declined due to habitat-shrinkage and large-scale poaching for alleged aphrodisiac properties of its horn. Its slow rate of breeding and predation of young by carnivores are perhaps also responsible for the depletion in its number. However, due to all possible protective measures accorded to it, its population is increasing steadily in various forest-reserves and sanctuaries especially in Kaziranga and Manas (Assam) and Jaldapara (West Bengal). According to a recent estimate of 1978 its total number stands over 900 individuals in the Kaziranga National Park.

LESSER ONEHORNED RHINOCEROS

48.   **Rhinoceros sondaicus** Desmarest   (E)

The Lesser Onehorned Rhinoceros is a dusky grey animal. It is slightly smaller in length, though rarely shorter at the shoulder than the Great One-horned Rhinoceros. The surface of its body is divided into shields by folds of skin as in the previous species, but the hide is divided by cracks into small, polygonal discs. The fold in front of the shoulders, however, extends right across the back. The single horn is never very long, measures rarely up to 27-28 cm. The horn generally is wanting in the female, but if present, it is only a low boss.

90

lesser onehorned rhinoceros

Distribution : This rhino was once known from Bengal and Assam, south of the Brahmaputra in India, and eastwards extended up to Sumatra, Java and Borneo. At present, it is said to occur in Java only.

Habits and habitat : It is more an inhabitant of tree-forest than of grass land, yet it is known to occur in a few swampy areas too. Its occurrence at higher elevations up to 2135 m is recorded. It is mostly a browser, unlike *Rhinoceros unicornis* which is a grazer.

Status : Extinct in India, Burma and eastern areas up to Malaysia. A few dozen individuals, however, still exist in western Java.

ASIATIC WILD ASS

49. Asinus hemionus khur (Lesson)   (E)

The Asiatic Wild Ass is slightly larger than the domestic ass in size, measuring 200-210 cm in the head and body length and 110-120 cm in height at the shoulder. The tail is tufted at the tip. The tips of ears are black. A dark brown mane continues as a stripe along the back to the base of the tail. The colour of its coat varies from rufescent grey to fawn or pale chestnut above and white below. Occasionally there is a dark cross stripe on the shoulder and faint rufous bars are said to occur on the limbs.

Distribution : In India, the Wild Ass is known from the Little Rann of Kutch. It is also reported to occur in Pakistan.

Habits and habitat : In India, it inhabits flat, salt-encrusted, sterile, arid country in the Rann of Kutch, where low xerophitic trees, grass and scrubs grow. It is found in small or large parties of over 30 individuals, remains inactive during the hottest part of the day and feeds in the early morning and late afternoon. It also raids cultivations at night. The usual rutting season is June-July or even later. The foal, one in number, is born after about 11 months of gestation.

Status : The Wild Ass used to occur in the past in thousands from northwestern India to Iran. In the last two hundred years, however, it has vanished from many areas, including Rajasthan. It is now in an endangered state. The population of about 5000 individuals in the Rann of Kutch, estimated in 1946, has now drastically run down to below one thousand.

wild ass

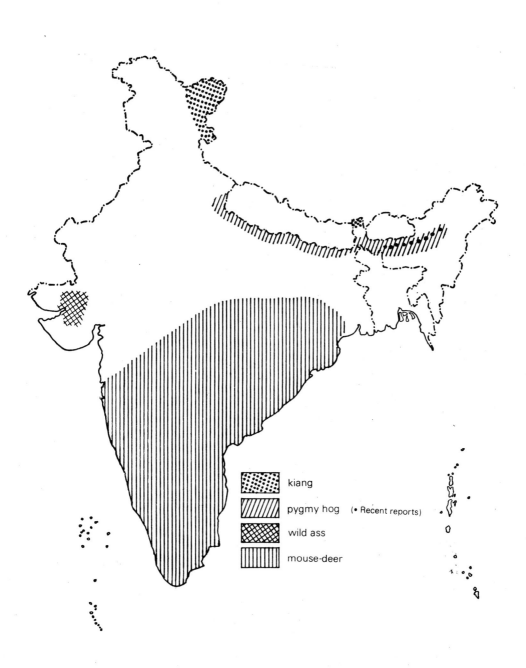

kiang

pygmy hog   (• Recent reports)

wild ass

mouse-deer

93

KIANG

50. Asinus kiang (Moorcroft) (E)

The Kiang is larger in size and in general darker and redder in colour than the Asiatic Wild Ass. The middorsal stripe is comparatively narrower. and without a whitish border. Moreover, it is also distinguished by the absence of the shoulder stripes. The hooves are large like those of the horses.

Distribution : It occurs in Tibet and Tibetan facies of India in Ladakh and Sikkim.

Habits and habitat : The Kiang lives in pairs or in small parties of a dozen or so in snowy, dry, cold deserts in very high plateau region.

Status : In India, the status of the Kiang is endangered, as its population has greatly run down due to natural calamities, and disturbances in the habitat.

kiang

Order Artiodactyla

ANDAMAN WILD PIG

51. Sus scrofa andamanensis Blyth (V)

The Andaman Wild Pig is much shorter than the mainland pig, and measures 51-52 cm in height at the shoulder. It is characterized by an indistinct crest over the neck and back. Its snout is elongated, with a terminally expanded flat disc bearing the nostrils. Its tail is very short, almost equal in length to its hindfoot and tufted with brown hair at the tip. The body colour of the pig is generally black, with brownish grey tips on some dorsal hair.

Distribution : It is known from Andaman Islands (Middle, South and Little Andaman and Havelock Islands).

Habits and habitat : This pig is a denizen of the forested area, but occasionally visits cultivated fields. Omnivorous in diet, it lives on crops, roots, tubers, insects, offal and the carrion.

Status : Shrinkage of habitat due to human encroachment for making new settlements, cultivation, timber works, etc., and uncontrolled killing of the animal for its meat have drastically brought down the population of the Andaman Wild Pig to a vulnerable state in the last few decades.

andaman wild pig

Andaman Islands

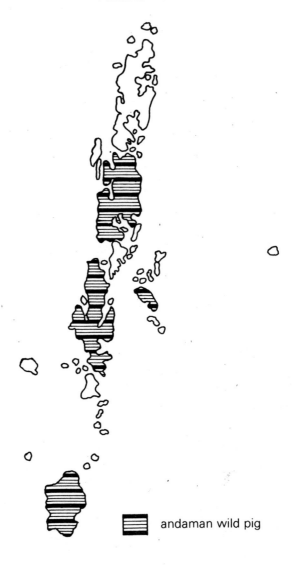

andaman wild pig

PYGMY HOG

52. **Sus salvanius** (Hodgson) (E)

Smallest of the known wild pigs, the Pygmy Hog measures between 65 and 70 cm in total length including the tail which is only 3-4 cm long. The height of this animal at the shoulder varies from 27 to 30 cm. The hair on the body are scanty and small, and those on the hinder portion of the neck and middle of the back are somewhat longer but do not form a crest. Its body colour varies from brown to blackish brown. The ears are small and naked.

Distribution : At present, it is known from the Duars of northern Assam only, though sometimes back it occurred in wide areas in the north along the Terai and Duars of the Himalaya, as far west as the Siwalik foothills of Nepal.

Habits and habitat : The Pygmy Hog is very seldom seen. It is found in tall grass-jungles and comes out of it at night only. It lives in small parties of 5 to 20 individuals, and an adult male leads the herd. It feeds on roots and bulbs, and also on small birds and their eggs, lizards, insects, etc. Three to

pygmy hog

four individuals are delivered per brood and the adults prepare nests within the grass jungles for the care of their young ones.

Status : It is a highly endangered species now, due to decimation of its population. The main reasons for the alarming situation of its status are the habitat destruction for extension of human settlement, agriculture, cutting and burning of the thatches, etc., and its random killing for meat. Efforts are being made for the conservation of this species in its natural habitat, especially in the Manas Wildlife Sanctuary and Baranadi and Nonai Reserve Forests in Darrang district of Assam. According to a recent estimate 30-40 hogs are present in the Baranadi Reserve Forest.

MOUSE-DEER
53. **Tragulus meminna** (Erxleben) (V)

The Mouse-Deer is much smaller than a Spotted Deer in size, measuring 45-56 cm in the head and body length and 25-31 cm in standing height at the shoulder. Its tail is very small, being 2-4 cm in length. It has slender limbs and high hindquarter. Like the Musk Deer, it is furnished with a pair of tusks which are better developed in males. Antlers are absent in this species. The colour of its body is brown, speckled with yellow; the undersurface is

mouse-deer

white. The sides of the body bear elongated white and buff spots. Three white stripes are present on its throat.

Distribution : This species occurs in southern India, and through eastern part of Madhya Pradesh and Orissa to Chhota Nagpur area in Bihar. It is also found in Sri Lanka.

Habits and habitat : It is a solitary creature, seclusive and crepuscular in habits. It keeps among rocks up to an elevation of 1850 m and rarely ventures to visit open areas from its hideout inside the forest. The male remains with the female during rut from June to July. The young ones, two in number, are born at the commencement of the winter.

Status : The Mouse-Deer is seldom seen now a days in much of the area of its occurrence, as it is being hunted by man for flesh, as also due to predation by carnivores.

MUSK DEER

54. Moschus moschiferus Linnaeus   (E)

The Musk Deer holds a place between the true deer and the antelope and is distinguished by its small head, pointed face, large ears, a small tail and by the absence of antlers and facial glands. Hindlimbs are considerably longer than the forelimbs. Hooves are well-adapted to trod on snow covered rocky ground. Male possesses a pair of curved tusks and globular musk gland situated beneath the skin of the abdomen near the navel. Its coat consists of thick, bristly and pithy hair with a shade of sepia brown to golden red, speckled with grey.

Distribution : It inhabits the dry temperate mountain forests of central and northeast Asia. Within India, it occurs throughout the Himalaya from Kashmir to Arunachal Pradesh at altitudes between 2338 and 3810 m. Extralimitally, it is found in northern Burma, Tibet and southern China.

Habits and habitat : The Musk Deer usually prefers to live in birch forest zone, either singly or in pairs. It frequents wooded slopes, often very steep. Though nocturnal in habit, it moves about to feed in the mornings and evenings. Its chief food items are lichens, ferns, flowers, leaves and grasses. The breeding season so far ascertained is during December or January, gestation period approximates six months, and usually a single fawn, occasionally twin, is born around May-June. Female attains sexual

musk deer

maturity within 16-17 months and the male becomes sexually mature after two to three years when it begins to secrete musk.

    Status : Ruthless persecution of this deer for musk has reduced its population to an extremely low level and is endangered now. However, due to enforced protection measures adopted by the Government, proposed method of collecting musk without killing the animal and increasing use of synthetic products, the chance of further depletion of its natural population has been reduced.

100

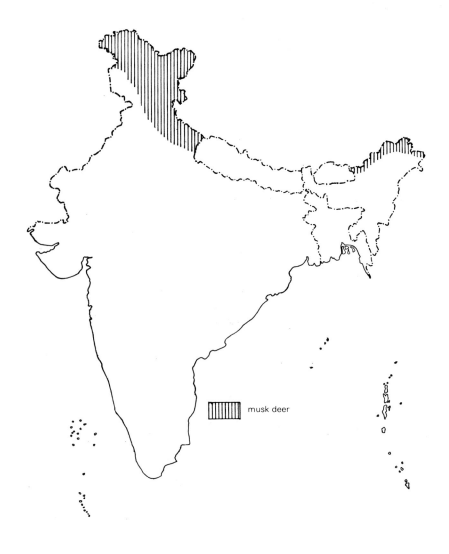

musk deer

SWAMP DEER

55. **Cervus duvauceli** G. Cuvier   (E)

The swamp Deer, a splendid deer with branched antlers, is a little smaller and lighter in body colour than those of the Sambar; measures about 180 cm in the length of head and body, 105-130 cm in height at the shoulder, and 20-23 cm in the length of tail. The stags have much-branched antlers. The brow tine is nearly at right angle to the beam. The beam remains unbranched for more than half its length, then it divides and subdivides into 10 –12 tines. Its coat is fine and woolly. The neck is maned. The body colour varies from brown to yellowish brown in winter and paler

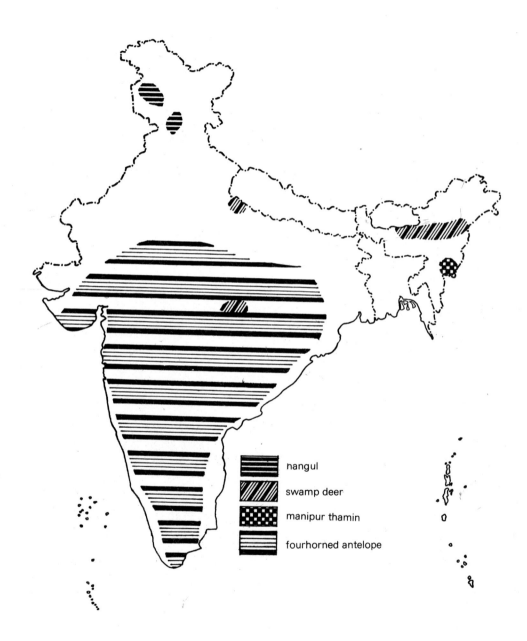

hangul

swamp deer

manipur thamin

fourhorned antelope

during the summer. It may develop white spots, similar to that found on the body of its fawn.

Two subspecies are recognised — the swamp-dwelling form which has splayed hooves to negotiate the swamps and the other which lives in hard open ground is provided with well-knit hooves.

Distribution : The Swamp Deer is found in the Terai and Duars of the northern and eastern India, from Uttar Pradesh to Assam and in the Kanha National Park in Madhya Pradesh as far southeast as Bastar.

Habits and habitat : It occurs in the swampy or dry grasslands in the Sal forest and may also be found on the outskirts of wood and on flat or undulating grounds. It is gregarious, and browses in large herds. During rutting season in winter, it congregates into large herds of 30-50 or several hundred individuals. By February-March the master stags, with horns in velvet or partly developed, are seggregated into smaller herds or singly. The period of gestation is about six months. It gives birth usually to a single young.

Status : About a hundred years back, the Swamp Deer used to occur extensively in the sub-Himalayan region, in the Indo-Gangetic plains from Sunderbans in the east to Sind (Pakistan) in the west, and throughout the area between the Ganga and Godavari rivers. At present its number has drastically reduced and the species is endangered, due to shrinkage of its habitat, predation, killing for its flesh, etc. The estimated number in Kanha was between 130-140 in 1977, in Kaziranga about 250 and in Dudwa (Uttar Pradesh) around 2000 (Sankhala, 1979).

swamp deer

MANIPUR THAMIN

56. Cervus eldi eldi M'Clelland (E)

The Manipur Thamin, popularly known as 'Sangai', is a Sambar-like deer with graceful antlers, arising from close-set pedicels. Standing height of this animal varies from 115 to 120 cm at the shoulder but the female is a little smaller than the male. Its antler measures between 102 and 107 cm in length, has an extremely long brow-tine, which joins the main beam in such a manner that the two form a continuous curve at right angles to the pedicel. The beam remains unbranched for more than half its length and after that two to three or as many as ten terminal tines come out of it. Its hair are coarse in summer and shaggy in winter. The colour, in male, is dark brown in winter and fawn in summer; the female is light fawn and the young is spotted.

Distribution : It is restricted to the Keibul Lamjao National Park in Manipur.

Habits and habitat : The Manipur Thamin possesses great speed in movement and acute vision, which aids it in its protection. It prefers open scrub jungle and floating swamp between rivers and hills. The present habitat of Sangai does not exceed 16 sq. km at the Kaibul Lamjao National

manipur thamin

Park. It comes out for feeding in the mornings and evenings in thick, forested parts; also occasionally, raids crops in the fringe of the forests. Its favourite food is the Tshing Kombong grass *(Saccharum latifolium)*. The male starts sheding its antlers in June and the latter are cleared of velvet by December. The rutting season starts in February-March and the young, usually one at a time, is born in October or so. Master stags are seldom noticed with the herd after the rut is over.

Status : Earlier accounts show that this deer was widely distributed in Manipur and was found in almost all the marshes of this State. In 1951 it was regarded as extinct, but subsequently in 1952-53 it was located once again in the floating swamps of Keibul Lamjao area in Manipur. The increase in human settlement, extension of cultivation, burning and cutting of thatch grass in the dry season have lead to the shrinkage of its favourite habitat and this coupled with accelerated poaching have driven them into this swampy area.

The total number of this deer was about 100 in 1954 and was reduced to almost half in 1966, due to severe flood in the area. Its population was estimated to be around 50 in 1974 by the Zoological Survey of India party, and it finally reduced to 18 in 1977. However, due to protective measures adapted by the State Forest Department, its number marginally increased to 23 in 1978. Another 49 individuals are present in different zoos of the country. Although certain measures have been adopted to reestablish it, but much more efforts are required to save this deer from extinction.

HANGUL
57.   Cervus elaphus hanglu Wagner   (V)

The Kashmir Stag or Hangul is a large deer, with a pair of spreading antlers; measures 120-130 cm in standing height at the shoulder, and 230-232 cm in the length of head and body. Each antler has generally five to six tines, sometimes more; the second tine considerably exceeds the first tine in length. Its coat colour varies from light to dark brown, with white rump patch or 'caudal disc' which extends for a short distance over the tail. The sides and limbs are paler and the chin and ears whitish. The body colour fades during summer.

Distribution : The Hangul is found in the northern side of Kashmir valley (at present restricted to Dachigam) and north Chamba, Himachal Pradesh.

Habits and habitat : It occurs singly or in small parties of 2-18 individuals in dense forests or in the riverine areas of lower Dachigam at elevations between 1750 and 3650 m. During winter, it collects into large herds and move to lower elevations. The stag sheds its antlers around March and the new ones get perfection by September. The rut starts by mid-September and ends by the end of October. The stag establishes a harem. The young is born in April-May. Several females give birth in the vicinity of each other.

Status : Factors such as, wanton destruction of habitat, cattle grazing, extension of cultivation, human interference in the area of its occurrence, etc., have caused depletion in the population of the Hangul. From an estimated number of 3000 in 1940, its number ran down between 140 and 170 in 1970. However, after the start of the IUCN Project in the same year and effective implementation of the conservation plan, the population has increased to 482 in 1983.

hangul

FOURHORNED ANTELOPE

58. Tetracerus quadricornis (Blainville) (V)

The Fourhorned Antelope or Chousingha, as its name signifies, possesses four horns on the head, which are smooth. The posterior pair of horns, about 8-10 cm in length, are situated on the top of the head, and the anterior pair, about 2-3 cm long or even smaller, are located on the forehead between and above the eyes. The female is without any horn. The standing height of the antelope is about 65 cm at the shoulder. The fur is thin, harsh and short. Its coat colour varies from brown to rufous brown above, and white below. A dark stripe runs down the front of each leg.

Distribution : The Chousingha is found in the peninsular India, extending north to Rajasthan and northeast to Bihar and Orissa. There is no report of its occurrence in the Malabar coast.

Habits and habitat : It is found singly, or in pair, in wooded and hilly country, near water. It is nocturnal, shy in nature and is never seen in dense forests. While walking or running it moves very quickly with a peculiar jerky action. It ruts during the rains; the gestation period varies between 240 and 255 days, and the young ones, one or two in number, are born around January-February.

Status : The population of the Fourhorned Antelope has considerably depleted over the years and is now rarely seen where it was once common. It is at present considered to be vulnerable due to shrinkage of its habitat and poaching for its flesh.

fourhorned antelope

GAUR

59. **Bos gaurus** H. Smith (V)

The Indian Bison possesses a heavy body, relatively short limbs, a prominent muscular ridge from shoulder to the middle of back, an ashy forehead and white feet. Standing height, in male is 175-196 cm at the shoulder; the female is slightly smaller. Its horn is almost a half-circle with a slight posterior bend at the tip and measures 68-76 cm along the curve. Horns of a cow are narrower than those of a bull. The old bull is black and almost hairless, but the cow is dark or reddish brown and possesses short hair.

Distribution : It occurs from Nepal to Arunachal Pradesh, thence south to Nagaland, Assam, Mizoram, Duars of West Bengal, Bihar, Orissa and in peninsular India. Extralimitally, it is known from Burma to Malaysia.

Habits and habitat : The Gaur occurs in herds of 6-12 individuals or more, in dense tropical forests. It ascends hills up to 1800 m or so. The chief food items of this animal are grasses, young bamboo-shoots, leaves and bark of trees. It forages from late evening to early morning in forest glades and open meadows. Mating takes place in winter or in early spring and usually one calf is born in a litter during September-October. Interbreeding of the Gaur with domestic cattle yields hybrid-cattle known as *gayal* or *mithan* in Arunachal Pradesh, Nagaland and Assam.

gaur

Status : The Gaur is reported to die in large numbers due to rinderpest and foot-and-mouth disease, both of which are transmitted to them by domestic cattle grazing in forests. Moreover, due to shrinkage of its habitat and its persecution, the population of gaur has come down to a vulnerable state, and exists in scattered herds in forests of Tamil Nadu, Kerala, Karnataka, Madhya Pradesh, Bihar, West Bengal, Assam and Nepal. The total estimated population is around 5000 individuals.

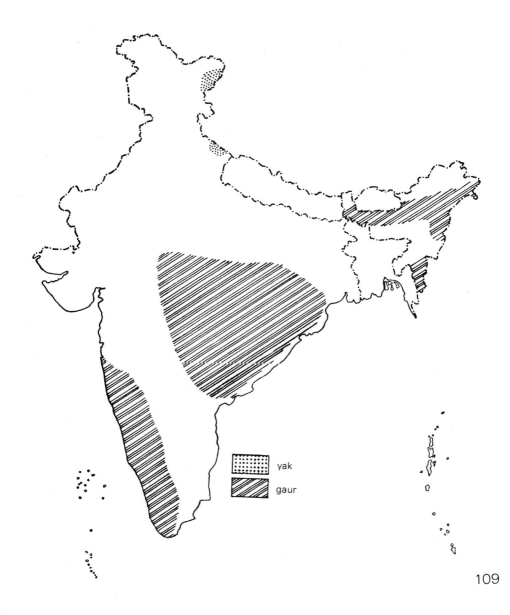

yak

gaur

YAK

60. Bos mutus (Przewalski) (E)

The wild Yak is as massive as the bison. It has a drooping head, a straight back, short sturdy limbs and is high at the shoulder. Its ears are small. A dewlap is absent. A full grown male measures 170-185 cm in standing height. Horns are smooth and round and are projected forward with the tip curved upward. The body is covered with hair which are very long on the neck, shoulder, lower part of each side, thigh and the terminal half of the tail. A tuft of hair is present between the two horns. Body colour is blackish brown with a little white about the muzzle.

Distribution : It occurs in Tibet and in parts of Kansu in China. Within the Indian limits the wild yak is found in Changchenmo Valley in Ladakh and sometimes reported to stray into northern Kumaon Hills. However, the domesticated yak is seen throughout the high altitudinal areas of the Himalaya.

Habits and habitat : The Yak inhabits the coldest, most desolate and rugged snow covered areas. In winter, it moves about in small herds and during the spring and summer large herds are seen feeding on rough wing grass grown in the valleys. It drinks plenty of water and during the winter even eats snow. It ruts during the post-monsoon period and gives birth to young in April-May.

Status : The wild Yak population has severely depleted, as its flesh is largely used for human consumption, and its skin and hair are utilized for making tents, outer garments and ropes. Though the exact population is not known, the yak appears to be highly endangered and only a small number may be found in isolated pockets within the Indian range of its occurrence.

yak

WILD BUFFALO

61.   Bubalus bubalis (Linnaeus)   (E)

   The Wild Buffalo is a robust, slaty black animal, much like the domestic buffalo, but has a straight back and dirty white feet. A grown up bull measures 1.5-2.8 m in height at the shoulder and about 4.5 m from the tip of the snout to the root of tail. Horns of the wild buffalo spread horizontally or curve upwards in a semicircle, and are triangular in cross-section and

wild buffalo

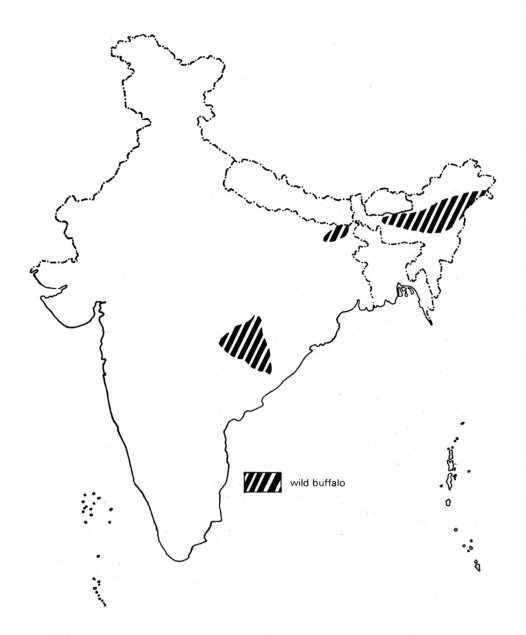

wild buffalo

transversely ridged. Their length may reach up to two metres. Horns of a cow are longer, but those of the bull are more massive.

Distribution : It occurs in the grass jungles of Nepal Terai extending eastwards to the plains of the Brahmaputra in Assam and Arunachal Pradesh. It is also found in Raipur and Bastar districts of Madhya Pradesh, western Orissa and eastern Maharashtra.

Habits and habitat : The Wild Buffalo is found in small herds in the swampy grass-jungles. It is the most ferocious of the Indian wild cattle, especially the cow with its newborn calf. During the dry season it wanders in search of food and is likely to enter the cultivated fields where it is reported to cause great damage. It feeds chiefly on grass in the morning and the evening, and during the day often lies down in shallow pools, with only parts of its head seen above the surface. It ruts in the autumn and establishes a harem. Its gestation period is about 10 months and the calf is usually dropped in early summer.

Status : It is now a greatly endangered species due to shrinkage of its habitat, poaching, predation by tiger, death from contagious diseases, etc. The distribution of the species is now restricted to National Parks and Sanctuaries, and the total surviving wild population is less than 1000 individuals.

BLACKBUCK

62. Antilope cervicapra (Linnaeus) (E)

The Blackbuck is one of the loveliest Indian animals.The buck has a blackish brown or an almost black coat with white underparts. It measures 120 – 130 cm in the head and body length and 17 to 18 cm in the length of tail. Standing height is about 80 cm at the shoulder. The inside of the legs, the lower third of each flank, the chin, a patch around the eyes and inner side of the ears are white. The female is smaller, yellowish fawn above and white below, and invariably hornless. The male, however, possesses a pair of spirally twisted, closely ringed horns, 40-50 cm in length.

Distribution : The Blackbuck occurs throughout the Indian plains, the eastern limit being Chilka Lake in Orissa and southwards extends to Point Calimere, Tamil Nadu. It is, however, not known from the Malabar Coast. It is quite abundant in Rajasthan and Gujarat. Outside India, it is known from Pakistan.

Habits and habitat : The Blackbuck is usually seen in herds of 10 to 30 or even over a hundred individuals and prefers flat open ground covered

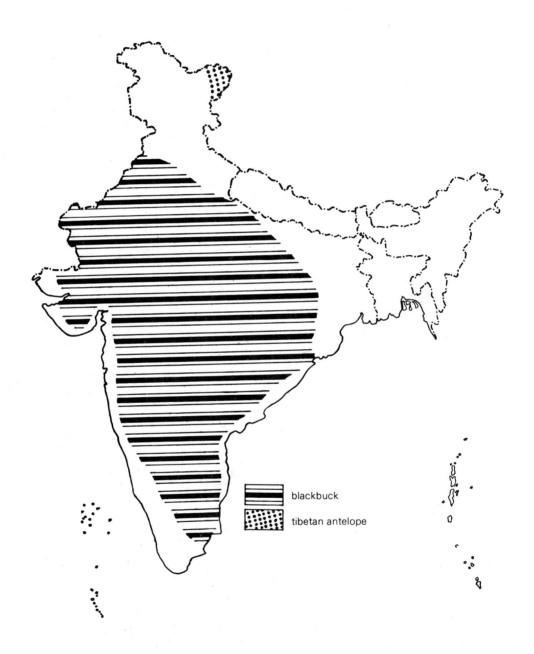

blackbuck

tibetan antelope

blackbuck

with grasses, bushes and scrubs but avoids forests and hilly tracts. It is said to be one of the fastest animals in the world and can reach to a speed of 100-104 km per hour and when alarmed moves off in a series of leaps and bounds. It feeds on grass, weak-stemmed plants, scrubs, pods of *Acacia,* fruits, etc. and grazes till noon and in the late afternoon. Each herd has a masterbuck, who may live in company with as many as fifty does or more. The rutting season is in the spring or winter; the gestation period is about five to six months.

Status : The Indian Antelope was once plentiful all over its range of occurrence, but has disappeared from many places where it was quite familiar a few decades ago. It is the gun that has killed them off in most places, for no other Indian animal has been more shot than the Blackbuck. Further, decimation of its population has been accelerated due to rapid agro-industrial development in its preferred habitat throughout the country. Outside protected areas, it is now seen in small herds only. However, after the enforcement of the Indian Wildlife (Protection) Act, its population is increasing steadily in the favourable habitats.

TIBETAN ANTELOPE OR CHIRU

63. **Pantholops hodgsoni** (Abel)   (V)

The Chiru is a rufous brown or pale fawn antelope whose body is covered with thick wool. Its face is black and the underside white. A black or dark brown stripe runs down the front of each leg. The standing height of the buck is about 80 cm at the shoulder and is 130-140 cm in the head and body length. Its muzzle is characteristically swollen in male and the nostril is furnished inside with an extensive sac. It possesses scent glands in the hooves and inguinal glands. Horns, in male, are long, erect, arising close together and are slightly curved forward and ringed in front but not behind, and measure 60-65 cm in length. The female is without horns.

Distribution : This species occurs throughout the Tibetan plateau from 3600 to 5500 m elevation and crosses into the Changchenmo Valley and a few other valleys nearby Ladakh by way of the Lanak La Pass.

Habits and habitat : The Chiru is generally seen solitary or in small parties of three to four individuals, sometimes in large herds of hundred or so. It keeps to flat areas and open valleys and feeds during the morning and the evening on the patches of grass in the vicinity of streams and rivers. It is a shy and wary animal, and during the day rests on some higher flats, in which it digs hollow deep enough to conceal its body. It mates during the winter and produces a single young in the summer.

Status : The population of the Tibetan Antelope has greatly reduced due to increased human interference in the area of its occurrence.

tibetan antelope

CHINKARA

64. Gazella dorcas (Linnaeus) (V)

The Chinkara is a slender bodied antelope. It measures about 65 cm in height at the shoulder. The horns, in male, are relatively longer than in the female, slightly curved and closely ringed; they measure about 25-30 cm in the buck and 10-13 cm in the doe. Its coat colour varies from sandy brown to light chestnut.

Distribution : It occurs in the plains and low hills of north western and central India, extending southwards to a little south of Krishna river. Extralimitally, it is found in Pakistan, middleeast Asian countries and westwards in northern Africa.

Habits and habitat : The Chinkara lives in small herds of 10 to 20 individuals or less, sometimes just two or three animals together. It is an animal of thin forested areas, preferring ravines, broken country, rocky areas and scrub-covered hills. It is also common in the sand-dunes of the desert zone. It is a very shy animal. Its sense of sight, scent, and hearing is equally well developed. When alarmed, the Chinkara runs at a wild pace till it finds a cover behind the bushes or in ravines. The food consists of grass, leaves, succulent fruits such as pumpkins, melons, etc. It is able to meet its water requirements from the sap of the vegetation it takes and from dew. However, it drinks freely when water is available. The female is often seen accompanied by one or two fawns.

Status : The population of the Chinkara in India is highly affected due to high rate of predation, random killing for its flesh and skin, and habitat-destruction for human settlements and agro-industrial use.

chinkara

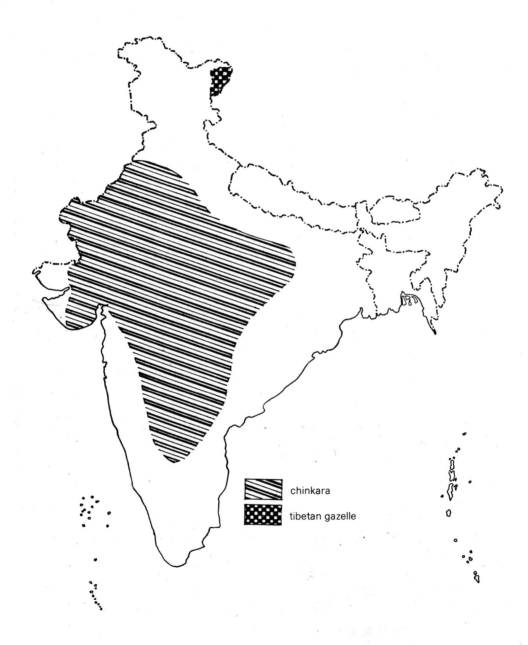

chinkara

tibetan gazelle

118

TIBETAN GAZELLE

65. **Procapra picticaudata** Hodgson   (E)

The Tibetan Gazelle, an antelope of the temperate region, measures about 60 cm in height at the shoulder and about 110 cm in the head and body length. Its coat is short and grey-coloured in the summer, dense and sandy fawn in the winter. The underparts are white but not sharply contrasting with the colour of the back. A white rump patch extends all round the base of the tail, forming a 'caudal disc'. The tail is short with a blackish tip. Horns, in bucks, rise vertically, curve sharply backwards and have 25-30 annulations. Each horn measures 30-33 cm in length. The female is without horns.

Distribution : This gazelle is known from northeastern Ladakh and hills north of Kumaon and Sikkim.

Habits and habitat : It inhabits the bleak Tibetan plateau at altitudes from 3950 to 5500 m in small parties varying from two to 12 individuals. Though its habits are very similar to those of the other gazelles of the plains, yet it is not very shy and is little frightened by noise. It ruts in December and one or two young ones are born in May.

Status : The population of the Tibetan Gazelle has depleted to an endangered stage, due to hunting of this animal for its flesh and skin, especially for its long and soft winter fur.

tibetan gazelle

TAKIN

66. Budorcas taxicolor Hodgson (E)

The Takin is a heavily built animal, with a large head, convex face, hairy muzzle, thick neck and stout limbs. It measures about 198 cm in the head and body length and 105-110 cm in height at the shoulder. Its tail is short as of a goat. Its thick legs are provided with large lateral hooves. The horns, in male, are thick, arise close together, curve outwards and then make a sharp turn pointing backwards. The horns are smaller in the female. The body colour of an adult male varies from yellowish white to golden yellow merging into deep reddish brown on the flanks and forequarter; the head is black. The female is greyer.

Distribution : Within the Indian limits it is known from Mishmi Hills in Arunachal Pradesh. Extralimitally, it occurs in Bhutan, northern Burma and possibly up to southern Kansu in China.

Habits and habitat : The Takin lives singly or in large herds on the steep mountain slopes, among thick bamboo and rhododendron forests, at elevations ranging from 2100 to 3000 m or so. In the Mishmi Hills, it also frequents tropical forests as low as 900 m. In the winter, it breaks up into small parties. It mates in July or August and the young, usually one, is dropped during March-April.

Status : Its population has drastically come down as it is being indiscriminately killed for its flesh and hide.

takin

120

goral

takin

GORAL

67. **Nemorhaedus goral** (Hardwicke) (V)

The Goral is a stockily built goat-like animal, having an antelope-like face and bell-shaped ears. It measures approximately 100-105 cm in the head-and-body length and 65-70 cm in shoulder-height. Its tail is relatively longer than that of a wild goat, barely extending below the level of belly. Both the sexes have conical, backwardly curved horns, 12-15 cm in length, marked with rings. Its hair are coarse and a conspicuous crest is present on its neck. The body colour of Goral varies from yellowish grey to rufous brown suffused with black; white patches are, however, present on the upper lip, chin, throat and the cheek.

Distribution : In India, Goral is found throughout the Himalaya at elevations between 914 and 2438 m, often near human habitation. Extralimitally, it occurs as far north as southeastern Siberia, thence through Korea to southern Burma. Swat in Pakistan is the western limit of its occurrence.

Habits and habitat : The Goral lives in small parties of four to eight individuals; old males are generally solitary. It feeds on the rugged, grassy hill sides during the morning and the evening and often invades terraced cultivation. Its mating season is during the winter, and a single young is born in May or June.

Status : This species is now vulnerable as it is being hunted by man for flesh and is preyed upon by various carnivores.

goral

HIMALAYAN TAHR

68. Hemitragus jemlahicus (H. Smith) (E)

The Himalayan Tahr is a heavy bodied mountain goat with long robust limbs and narrow erect ears. The buck measures about one metre in standing height at the shoulder and the doe is a little shorter. Its body is covered with long hair, and the neck and shoulder with still longer hair which form a shaggy mane, reaching to the knee. Horns of this animal are curved backwards. These are closely set, compressed, slightly wrinkled transversely except at the tip and keeled in front. Its coat-colour is reddish brown. However, young animals are greyish brown and the kids pale.

Distribution : This species occurs in the Himalaya from the Pir Panjal range in Kashmir to Bhutan.

Habits and habitat : The Himalayan Tahr is a forest loving animal. It prefers to live in herds, on steep rocky slopes covered with trees of oak and ringal cane, at elevations between 3050 and 3660 m. It comes out of the forest in the evening and goes to rest before sunrise. Mating takes places in winter when it comes down to the valley, and a single young is born during the summer.

Status : This species is endangered due to excessive killing for its flesh and skin. Schaller counted 45 individuals in a three-weeks trip around Kang Chu Valley in eastern Nepal in 1975. Survey parties of the Zoological Survey of India encountered small herds of the Himalayan Tahr in several areas of Sikkim and in the Neora Valley in West Bengal, during 1979-1983.

himalayan tahr

himalayan tahr

nilgiri tahr

NILGIRI TAHR

69.   Hemitragus hylocrius (Ogilby)   (E)

The Nilgiri Tahr is a stocky wild goat, resembling the Himalayan Tahr in appearance. Standing-height of the buck is from 1.0 to 1.1 m at the shoulder; the female is, however, a little shorter. Its horns are transversely wrinkled. They are almost in contact at the base, rise parallel for some distance, then diverge and curve downwards. An old buck is dark brown, almost black, with a grizzled or white saddle patch on the loin and the doe is yellowish grey. Its undersurface is paler. The male possesses a short mane on the ridge of the neck and shoulder.

Distribution : This Tahr's present range of distribution is restricted to the States of Tamil Nadu and Kerala between Nilgiri Hills and Ashambu Hills. In between these hills it occurs in isolated pockets along the crest of the ranges of Western Ghats at elevations between 1300 and 2600 m.

Habits and habitat : Nilgiri Tahr occurs in herds of 5-50 individuals, amongst the crags, rocky precipices and grass-covered hills. It keeps itself above the forest and rarely enters woods, and forages in the early mornings and evenings. The breeding season appears to extend throughout a greater part of the year and the kids are found with the herds in most months. The female is said to produce two young ones at a birth.

Status : The population of the Nilgiri Tahr has depleted to an alarming stage, mainly due to poaching for its excellent flesh. Moreover, predation by various carnivores, destruction of its habitat for establishment of new settlements, plantations, timber, etc., as also diseases in wild population have brought down the number of Nilgiri Tahr to an endangered level. According to an estimate made in 1977, the population of Tahr was around 2200 individuals or so.

IBEX

70. **Capra ibex** Linnaeus (E)

The ibex is a sturdy built goat. The standing height of the buck at the shoulder is about one metre and that of the doe a little less. The buck has a long beard. Horns are long, flat, curved backwards like a scimitar and bossed with bold ridges. These measure 1-1.5 m in full grown bucks, but only about 30 cm in a doe. Its coat is short and coarse in summer but has dense growth of underwool during the winter. The body colour varies with the season; during summer the male is dark brown, with irregular white patches and the female yellowish brown; in winter the colour becomes yellowish white tinged with grey.

Distribution : In India, Ibex is found in the western Himalaya from Kashmir to Kumaon in Uttar Pradesh. Extralimitally, it occurs in Europe and from Central Asia to China.

ibex

Habits and habitat : This species is found in herds of 10-50 individuals at elevations between 2660 and 6710 m but visits lower elevations in spring for grazing on new grass. It mates during winter, and a single or two kids are born in May or June.

Status : Underwool of the Ibex is a valuable product of commerce and is used in the preparation of superior quality shawls, stockings, gloves, etc. Ropes and blankets are made out of its coarse hair, and boots of its skin. A large number of these goats are, therefore, killed every year. As a result its population has so much decreased that the species is endangered now.

ibex

markhor

MARKHOR

71. Capra falconeri (Wagner) (E)

The Markhor is distinguished from other wild goats in India by its massive body, having thick and silky fur. Adult males are between 95 and 100 cm in height at the shoulder, the females are a little smaller. The buck, doe and the young have beard which however, is restricted to the chin in the doe and kids. The Markhor also has spectacular shaggy grey mane down the neck and the shoulder. Its horns are widely divergent, compressed and spirally twisted, having a keel in front. The approximate length of the horn along the outer curve is 1.2-1.5 m with a basal girth of 25-34 cm. Hair are rusty grey and long in winter, and reddish brown and short in summer, except in the old bucks which are almost white.

Distribution : This goat is known from Kashmir in western Himalaya, and is also reported from Pakistan, Afghanistan and southern Russian Turkestan.

Habits and habitat : The Markhor occurs in small or large herds of 12-50 individuals or more. It is found at elevations between 600 and 3600 m in association with juniper and birch forests. In the absence of protective underwool, it avoids the higher elevations frequenly visited by the Ibex.

markhor

Even when it grazes in the vicinity of the Ibex, there is no recorded physical interaction. It mates in winter and a single young or twins are born between May and June.

Status : The population of the Markhor has greatly depleted, due to its indiscriminate killing, continued habitat shrinkage for human need, grazing by domestic cattle, etc. Infections of contagious diseases also had an adverse effect on its number. At present herds of this goat are seen in some isolated pockets in the range of its occurrence. The main concentration of the Pir Panjal subspecies *(C. f. cashmiriensis)* is now in the Chitral Gol Sanctuary and Tushi valley just north of Chitral (Pakistan), which are estimated to hold about 150 and 125 heads respectively. However, the world population of the species is estimated to be between 2000 and 2500 (IUCN Red Data Book, 1972).

NAYAN

72. **Ovis ammon hodgsoni** Blyth   (V)

The Nayan is the largest of all the living sheep, the standing height of males being 1.07-1.20 m at the shoulder; the females are a little smaller. Horns, in male, are massive, coarsely wrinkled, subtriangular in cross section

nayan

nayan

crestless himalayan porcupine

and measure from 90 cm to 1 m; in the female these are shorter. Its coat colour is light brown, darker on the shoulders, and white on the throat, chest, belly, inner side of limbs and front side of legs below the knee. The male possesses a whitish ruff on the neck and a white caudal disc.

Distribution : This sheep is found in the Tibetan plateau facies from northern Ladakh (Kashmir) east to Bhutan, occasionally crossing over the Himalaya in Spiti (Himachal Pradesh), Kumaon (Uttar Pradesh) and Nepal.

Habits and habitat : It occurs in herds of 3-15 individuals at fairly high elevations (3700 m or above) and prefers to live in dry spots on rocky slopes with nearby feeding areas. It ruts during the late autumn and the young is born in May or June.

Status : Inspite of its alertness and great speed in movement, Nayan is being killed in large numbers for its flesh and wool. Hence, its present status is vulnerable.

URIAL

73.   Ovis orientalis Gmelin   (V)

The Urial is about the size of a domestic sheep, being 91 cm or so in height at the shoulder. Its coat colour varies from rufous grey or fawn in summer to mixed grey and brown during winter. Adult ram possesses a black or grizzled ruff, growing from either side of the chin and extends

urial

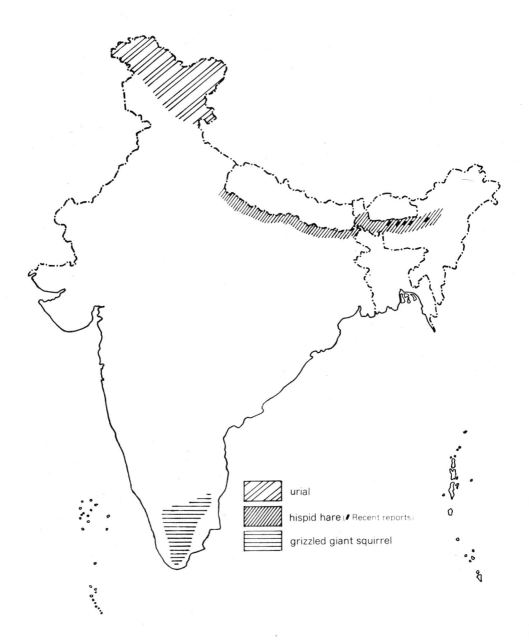

urial

hispid hare (▟ Recent reports)

grizzled giant squirrel

down the throat. Horns in ram, are thick, strongly wrinkled, triangular in cross section and curve backwards forming a semicircle. In Ladakh population, horns turn inwards at the tip and measure from 61 to 84 cm along the curve. Horns, in female, are short and nearly straight.

Distribution : The Urial is known from Kashmir in India, northern Tibet, Pakistan, Afghanistan and southern Iran.

Habits and habitat : It is found in flocks of 3-30 sheep, in the steep grassy hill slopes at moderate elevations. It is wary and active. Although it avoids precipices, but can get over the steep hills with wonderful ease. It ruts in September-October or even later, and generally a single, occasionally two lambs, are born in a litter around June.

Status : Its population has come down drastically due to human interference. It is being killed for its excellent flesh and wool. Moreover, its habit of free mixing with domestic sheep has an adverse effect on the wild population. Hence, its status is vulnerable.

Order Lagomorpha

HISPID HARE

74. Caprolagus hispidus (Pearson)   (E)

The Hispid Hare is almost of the size of the Blacknaped Hare, but differs from it in its fur being coarse and bristly as against soft in the latter. Its colour above is dark brown; the underparts are white except the chest which is brownish. The tail is brown throughout. The ears of this hare are short, about 7 cm or so. Its hindlegs are apparently shorter but exceed the forelegs in length. The length of its head and body ranges from 45 to 50 cm and that of the tail 4 to 5 cm.

Distribution : Once it occurred in the Terai and Duars ranging from Uttar Pradesh to Assam, Tripura and Bangladesh, but at present, it appears to be restricted to Duars area of West Bengal and Assam, and in Bangladesh.

Habits and habitat : This hare inhabits the grass jungle in the primeval *Sal* forest region. It is a slow moving animal and less endowed with the power of running at a fast rate. It lives singly or in pairs and seldom invades the cultivated fields where competition exists with the Blacknaped hare for foraging. It feeds mainly on roots, barks, young shoots, and leaves. It breeds twice or thrice in a year and the litter size is 2-5.

133

hispid hare

Status : Nothing is known about the exact population of the Hispid Hare. It was once a common animal in the area of its occurrence. Although reports of its occurrence in a few places in eastern India are received in recent years, the species has become very rare and greatly endangered, due to loss of its habitat for various reasons, and hunting by man for its flesh.

Order Rodentia

GRIZZLED GIANT SQUIRREL

75.Ratufa macroura dandolena Thomas & Wroughton (V)

The Grizzled Giant Squirrel is of large size and measures 29-41 cm in the head and body length and the tail is slightly longer than that. Dorsally, it is brownish, grizzled with white; its underparts, cheeks, a patch on the neck, arms and legs are buffy white, and the top of the head, shoulder and the toes are blackish brown. Its tail varies from brown to dark brown and is edged with white hair throughout its length, sometimes tending to be wholly pale terminally.

Distribution : The Grizzled Giant Squirrel occurs in the hill forests of Tamil Nadu and Sri Lanka.

Habits and habitat : This species inhabits high trees in dry deciduous and moist evergreen forests, rarely coming to the ground. It is diurnal in habit. Its diet consists of fruits, nuts, insects, etc. The young ones are born in a large, globular nest of twigs and leaves, constructed on a branch of a tree; the litter-size is one or two.

Status : The status of the Indian population of this squirrel is vulnerable, mainly due to the shrinkage of its habitat.

grizzled giant squirrel

CRESTLESS HIMALAYAN PORCUPINE
76. Hystrix hodgsoni (Gray) (R)

The Crestless Himalayan Porcupine is normally crestless, but occasionally possesses a few bristles, slightly longer than the neighbouring spines on the back of the neck. It is a fairly large rodent, the head and body length being about 47 cm and the tail 27 cm or so. It has powerful feet with sharp claws. Its body and the limbs are covered with short and grooved spines; intermixed with them are also present a few longer spines of the size of 20-25 cm on the loins and rump. The colour of its body is dark brown but blackish on the limbs. A narrow band of white-tipped spines forms a collar in front of its neck. The medial portion of its quills are dark brown, the tip or the base or both are whitish.

Distribution : Within the Indian limits, it is known from central and eastern Himalaya at elevations up to about 1500 m, ranging from Nepal through Sikkim to Nagaland and Manipur. It is said to occur in lower Bengal also. It also occurs in Burma and other countries of southeastern Asia including China.

Habits and habitat : The Chinese Porcupine lives in burrows dug by itself in hill slopes or in plain ground among bushes. It is nocturnal and seclusive in habits. Its foraging hours are early and late quarters of the night and feeds mainly on vegetative matter, such as roots, tubers, bulbs, etc. It is monogamous, breeds in spring and the litter size is usually two.

Status : The population of this species has greatly declined, mainly due to indiscriminate killing for its much esteemed meat and quills. At present, it is considered as a rare animal.

crestless himalayan porcupine

BLUE WHALE

77.   **Balenoptera musculus** Linnaeus   (E)

The Blue Whale is also called the Sulphurbottomed Whale, for its yellowish colour on the underside due to the presence of a thin film of diatoms. The general colour, however, is slate-blue mottled with blue-grey, with the tips and undersurface of the long and tapering flippers whitish. It is the largest living animal known and measures from 22.5 to 23.5 m or more in length, rarely as large as 34 m, with a corresponding weight of 80 to 81 tonnes. The weight up to 152 tonnes has also been recorded for this species. The body is streamlined and except a few hairs present on the lips, it is naked. The head is very long and the dorsal fin low and small. The ventral side has numerous grooves, generally 80-100 in number.The baleen plates, present in the Blue Whale, are characteristically jet black.

Distribution : The Blue Whale occurs in all the seas. So far the Indian subcontinent is concerned, it is known from the Bay of Bengal and the Arabian Sea.

Habits and habitat : It is pelagic and migratory in its movements. In summer, it moves to Arctic and Antarctic waters where planktonic crustacea, on which it mainly feeds, grow in profusion. In winter, it migrates to temperate region for breeding. Pregnancy in the Blue Whale occurs after every two or three years and normally one young is delivered at a time.

Status : This Whale has been so extensively hunted for commercial purposes that its number has severly depleted. Some protection has been provided to it now by delimiting its capture.

blue whale

SPERM WHALE

78.   Physeter catodon Linnaeus   (E)

The Sperm Whale, also called the Cachalot, is distinguished from all other cetaceans by its enormous square-cut head, with a blow-hole at its tip. The lower jaw is shorter than the upper one, narrow, and has about thirty large teeth. The males of this species grow to about 15-18 m and the females more than half of that. The dorsal fin is but a rounded hump; the flippers are broad and rounded. The tail is horizontally placed, wide and deeply notched. Its colour varies from grey to dark bluish grey or black; the underside is sometimes whitish.

Distribution : The Sperm Whale is found nearly in all the tropical and the subtropical seas, and sometimes visits the arctic waters. In Indian limit it is said to be common in the Bay of Bengal and off Sri Lanka.

Habits and habitat : The movement of this whale is more rapid than those of other whales. It can dive for a long time and to great depths. It is invariably found in open seas in small parties, but sometimes join to form large schools, and hunts mainly on squids and cuttle-fishes. The breeding season of the Sperm Whale in Northern Hemisphere is said to be from March to May, whereas in Southern Hemisphere between September and December. The gestation period is 15 to 16 months and a single young is delivered at a time.

Status : The Cachalot has been indiscriminately killed by man for spermaceti, sperm oil and ambergris it contains in its head, blubber and intestine respectively. The species is now considered to be endangered, for its population has run down to an alarming state.

sperm whale

COMMON DOLPHIN

79. Delphinus delphis Linnaeus   (I)

The Common Dolphin, like the Gangetic Dolphin *Platanista gangetica* (Lebeck), is a clipper-built, slim animal, with elongated snout forming the beak which is separated from the forehead by a prominent groove. It is about 2.5 m in total length. The dorsal fin is quite prominent and falcate. The pectoral fins are three times as long as broad, narrow in the distal half and acutely pointed. The colour of this commonest dolphin varies from black to dark grey above and whitish below. Along the sides of body it possesses prominent fulvous or ochre bands.

common dolphin

Distribution : This dolphin is a common one in all temperate and tropical seas, occasionally enters freshwater. In India, however, it is so far reported from the coastal waters of Andhra Pradesh, Tamil Nadu and Gujarat.

Habits and habitat : The Common Dolphin is an intelligent and social animal. It generally travels in schools of large number of individuals, jumping one after the other. It is very speedy in its movement and can easily keep pace with ships travelling at a speed of 30 knots and above. It feeds mainly on the marine fishes, especially the shoaling species, and cuttle-fishes. The gestation period is about nine months and the young is produced from winter to summer season.

Status : This dolphin is scarcely reported from Indian waters in recent years, and its status, so far India is concerned, is indeterminate.

GANGETIC DOLPHIN

80. **Platanista gangetica** (Lebeck)   (I)

The body of the Gangetic Dolphin is fusiform, with a pair of triangular pectoral flippers, rudimentary dorsal fin and a horizontally placed tail fluke. The head is prolonged into a compressed rostrum, which is shorter in male than in the female. The neck is short. Its body is blackish throughout and measures about two to three metres in the head and body length.

gangetic dolphin

Distribution : It is known to occur in Ganga, Brahmaputra and Indus rivers and their larger tributaries.

Habits and habitat : The Gangetic Dolphin is not gregarious yet several individuals may be seen in the same part of the river. It comes on the surface of water for breathing. It is common in tidal waters, but appears to undergo local migration. The jaw in this mammal is well-adapted for browsing in bottom muds and its main food items so far known are fishes and crustaceans. The period of gestation is about eight to nine months, and the young, a single or very rarely two in number, are born between April and July.

Status : Indeterminate, but its population has declined considerably in recent years due to pollution of tidal waters and loss of habitat as a result of silting. Moreover, it is captured by fishermen in parts of the country, for its flesh and oil.

Order Sirenia

DUGONG OR SEA-COW

81. Dugong dugon (Müller) (V)

The Sea-Cow is popularly called the Dugong, which name might have been derived from the Malayan word 'duyong'. It is quite different from the cetaceans, and measures about two to three metres in total length. The head of this animal is massive, with a small mouth and the upper lip projecting over the lower one in the form of a fleshy pad bearing long fine bristles. The nostrils are placed on top of the head, eyes small and deeply sunk, and the ear is just a small circular aperture. The Dugong has hardly any neck and its forelimbs are modified into flippers. Its tail fluke is horizontally placed. The incisors, called the tusks, are projected through the skin of the upper lip in male. The colour is dorsally grey, bluish grey or brownish grey.

Distribution : The Sea-Cow occurs in tropical waters and estuaries, and is distributed from Red Sea and East Africa in the west to New Guinea and Australia in the east. Within the Indian limits, it is, however, known along the western coastal area, the Gulf of Mannar, Palk Strait and around the Andaman Islands.

Habits and habitat : The Sea-Cow is pelagic, but rarely ascends rivers. It is clumsy and sluggish in habit, showing preference for warm and shallow coastal waters where it feeds on marine grass and algae. Its breeds probably throughout the year and the gestation period is about eleven months. Usually one young is produced at a birth and is carried on the back of the mother till maturity.

Status : The Sea-Cow is an economically important animal, for it provides oil, fat and meat for human use. However, due to its persecution in great numbers, it is becoming rare and at present its population appears to have run down to a vulnerable condition.

sea-cow

BIRDS

Order Ciconiiformes

EASTERN WHITE STORK

82. Ciconia ciconia boyciana Swinhoe (E)

The Eastern White Stork is a large-sized, egret-like bird with white and black plumage. Its standing height is about 106 cm. The scapulars and wing-quills are black but the rest of its plumage is white. It has a long neck. The legs are very long and bright red. The bill is large and black. The sexes are alike.

Distribution : The Eastern White Stork is a winter visitor in Assam and adjoining states of northeastern India, south to the Sundarbans. It also winters in Bangladesh. Its breeding area is from southern Ussuri and Amur rivers east to Korea and Japan.

eastern white stork

145

Distribution : The geographical distribution of the Large Whistling Teal is discontinuous. It is found in southern California and Mexico in North America, northern South America south to Paraguay and northern Argentina, eastern Africa, Malagasay, Pakistan, India, Sri Lanka, Bangladesh and Burma. Within the Indian Union this bird is widely but sporadically scattered, being relatively more common in West Bengal, Assam, Manipur and Tripura.

Habits and habitat : No specific data are available for the habits and habitat of the Eastern White Stork in its wintering ground in India. Presumably these are similar to those of the allied White Stork *(Ciconia ciconia ciconia)*. It is to be found in marshy grassland, drained out fallows and moist ploughed field. This is a very wary bird and is difficult to approach. It feeds on insects and their young ones, crustaceans, frogs, reptiles, rodents and also on fishes. It produces a characteristic bill-clattering sound.

Status : The Eastern White Stork was never a common winter visitor in India. It has not been reported from the Indian area later than the early part of the present century. The surviving population of this subspecies is small. As such, it should be considered as endangered.

Order Anseriformes

LARGE WHISTLING TEAL

83.   **Dendrocygna bicolor** (Vieillot)   (E)

The Large Whistling Teal is a pale brown, maroon-chestnut duck, slightly smaller than the domestic duck. Its length is about 51 cm. It can be distinguished from the more common Lesser Whistling Teal *(Dendrocygna javanica)* by the creamy white upper tail-coverts, a distinct black line along the back of the neck and a broad rusty whitish collar round the middle of the foreneck, besides being slightly larger. The female is slightly smaller and duller. The immature bird has the chestnut portions of the adult more brown.

large whistling teal

Habits and habitat : The Large Whistling Teal is a resident bird in India but is nomadic and is possibly locally migratory. It keeps in smaller flocks and is generally found in secluded wetlands containing floating and submerged aquatic vegetation, *e.g.,* duck-weeds, water lilies, etc. This duck is often found in mixed foraging parties with the Lesser Whistling Teal. Its food consists of aquatic weeds, tender shoots, wild and cultivated paddy, snails, crustaceans, worms, etc. Its call is said to be similar to that of the Lesser Whistling Teal but shriller. It breeds from June to October and makes its nest generally in the hollow of tree-trunks, sometimes on forks of branches of tall trees and occasionally on the ground among vegetation near the water.

Status : As per published reports, the Large Whistling Teal was fairly common in the past in northeastern India, more so in Nadia, Jessore and Khulna districts of erstwhile Bengal. But recent surveys indicate that this bird has become scarce as a result of shrinkage of its habitat by enhanced encroachment by man. In the western districts of Assam the bird still maintains some stronghold. The fate of this bird in India may, therefore, be considered as endangered.

ANDAMAN TEAL

84. Anas gibberifrons albogularis (Hume) (E)

The Andaman Teal is a bird almost the size of a Common Teal *(Anas crecca)*, with dark brown feathers edged with greyish, producing a scaly effect. It is about 43 cm in total length. The throat, foreneck and the area around the eyes are white. The speculum is green and black with a conspicuous white patch in front and a small band at the rear. The underparts are buffy grey, spotted with dark brown. The female is slightly duller with coppery green speculum. The immature bird is like the female but the markings on the underparts are less distinct and the white area around the eyes much narrower and with a fulvous wash.

Distribution : The Andaman Teal is endemic in the Andaman group of islands and some other nearby islands (Landfall, Great Coco, Coco, etc.).

Habits and habitat : The Andaman Teal is restricted to the tidal creeks, freshwater pools and swamps of oceanic islands. It is found in flocks of four to a dozen or sometimes more. It freely mixes, actively swims and forages with domestic ducks and lesser whistling teals. This teal spends most of the day perched on the mangrove trees or on rocks exposed during the low tide but from time to time takes to water for feeding. It feeds chiefly during the night. Its food consists mainly of plant material such as tender shoots of paddy and other crops, grains, etc. It also consumes insects, molluscs, worms, etc. The call is a whistle and sometimes a quack. It breeds during the monsoon months and lays eggs generally in the hollows of trees but nests are also made on the ground in grass by the side of pools and creeks.

andaman teal

Status : The Andaman Teal was quite common in most of the islands of the Andaman group during the middle of the last century. Since then its population has dwindled much mainly due to disturbances in and destruction of its habitat as a result of human settlement and large-scale hunting with fire-arms. It has been estimated that in the Middle Andaman Island, the supposed stronghold of this bird, there are only 200 to 300 individuals. The Andaman Teal, therefore, may be regarded as an endangered bird.

Andaman Islands

andaman teal

PINKHEADED DUCK

85.   Rhodonessa caryophyllacea (Latham) (Extinct)

The Pinkheaded Duck is of the size of a domestic duck. It is about 60 cm in length. In the adult male, the bill, partially tufted head and the neck are bright pink; the rest of the body is dark brown, with a pinkish buff speculum. The adult female is duller. Its bill, head and neck are suffused with bright pink but the pink coloured area is not sharply demarcated from the rest of the body which is dull brown. The speculum is pale brownish buff. The immature bird is lighter brown in colour and has the head and neck pale rosy white with the top of the head, nape and hindneck brown. The general features and postures of this duck are like those of a whistling teal. In body proportions and plumage pattern it is like a pochard while its feet are like those of a dabbling duck.

Distribution : The Pinkheaded Duck was a resident of northern and northeastern India (Orissa, Bihar, Bengal, Assam and Manipur) in the forested foothills of the Himalaya and the adjoining plains. Stragglers were sporadically recorded in winter from Punjab, Uttar Pradesh, Maharashtra, Andhra Pradesh and Tamil Nadu. Extralimitally, it is also known from Nepal, Burma and Tibet. In its residential range in India and Nepal it affected the marshes in the Himalayan Terai and Duars, and swampy lowland grass jungles.

Habits and habitat : The Pinkheaded Duck was generally met with singly or in small groups, and during the breeding season (May-July), in pairs. This bird was shy and secretive, and was rarely seen unless flushed by chance from ponds amongst tall grass jungles. This duck was a surface feeder. Its food consisted of aquatic organisms, both vegetable and animal matter.

pinkheaded duck

Status : The Pinkheaded Duck was probably never plentiful. Its population started declining as early as 1878, obviously due to shrinkage of its habitat and hunting. The last authentic sight record of it in India is June, 1935 (Darbhanga, Bihar). This beautiful species of duck, for all practical purposes, may be considered as extinct in India.

WHITEWINGED WOOD DUCK

86.   Cairina scutulata (S. Muller)   (V)

In body proportions, pattern of the head and neck, the Whitewinged Wood Duck is similar to the Comb Duck *(Sarkidiornis melanotos)* but differs from the latter in not having a comb on the bill, and the lower parts being

whitewinged wood duck

chestnut brown instead of white, presence of a white patch on the wing-shoulder and a blue-grey speculum. Its average length is about 81 cm. The sexes are more or less alike, the male having more gloss on the plumage, much larger and heavier and with orange-yellow iris instead of brown. The immature bird is much duller and browner.

Distribution : The Whitewinged Wood Duck formerly occurred in northeastern India, Bangladesh, Burma, Vietnam, Thailand, southeast through the Malaya Peninsula to Andalas (Sumatra) and Java. Within the Indian limits, the Whitewinged Wood Duck is to be found in the eastern districts of Assam (Nowgong, Sibsagar, Dibrugarh, North Lakhimpur Cachar), and Siang, Lohit and Tirap districts of Arunachal Pradesh. Its existence in Manipur is doubtful.

whitewinged wood duck

Habits and habitat : The Whitewinged Wood Duck is essentially a resident of the dense tropical evergreen forest. It prefers to live in inaccessible swampy areas formed by numerous rivers, streams, creeks, etc. This duck is generally found in pairs or in small parties of four to six, though parties of more than 10 are also recorded. It is a shade-loving bird keeping most of the day in secluded jungle pools, occasionally perching on the tree during the day. It moves for its feeding ground in open waters after dusk and remains active throughout the night till early morning. The food consists of both plant and animal material : aquatic plants, seeds of wild and cultivated plants, aquatic insects, crustaceans, molluscs and fishes. The usual call of the male is a trumpet-like *cronk* while the call of the female in flight is a whistle. It breeds in the hollows of trees, during summer months.

Status : During the last 50 years the population of the Whitewinged Wood Duck has dwindled much and from many areas it has disappeared. The Assam Valley Wild Life Society estimated in 1976 some 44 birds in whole of Assam, while its population, as per local information, has become quite thin in Arunachal Pradesh. It is encouraging to know that this bird has successfully bred in captivity at Slimbridge, U.K. (in 1969), in Bordubai Tea Estate (in 1977), and at the Gauhati Zoo Park in recent years. Possibilities of survival of this vulnerable species appear to be fair if bred in captivity and trial liberations undertaken in its natural habitat.

Order Falconiformes

HIMALAYAN GOLDEN EAGLE

87. Aquila chrysaetos daphanea Severtzov   (E)

The Himalayan Golden Eagle is a very large and graceful eagle. Its length is between 90 and 100 cm. The feathers of the hindcrown, nape and hindneck are lanceolate and blackish brown, and are tipped and edged with golden buff or tawny. The wings are mottled with buffy white. The tail has irregular bars at the base and has the tip darker. The upper and under tail-coverts, shoulder of wings and thighs are rufous-brown. Coloration in both the sexes are alike but the female is larger. The immature bird is glossy brownish black with the head and neck tawny.

Distribution : The Himalayan Golden Eagle is distributed approximately from eastern Iran, Afghanistan and Baluchistan to central Asia, south to the Himalaya east to Nepal, Bhutan and eastern Arunachal Pradesh, between 1850 and 5500 m elevation.

Habits and habitat : Within the Indian limits the Himalayan Golden Eagle is essentially an inhabitant of high mountainous terrain. Its flight is direct with powerful wing-beats coupled with long glides. It adopts somewhat falcon-like hunting method and usually stoops at its prey from a height with terrific velocity. It often hunts in pairs. This eagle feeds chiefly on pigeons, chukors, snowcocks, monals and other pheasants, foxes, marmots, pine martens, hares, flying squirrels, young bharals and fawns of musk deer. It also eats kids of tahr and lambs of domestic sheep. This eagle is silent by nature. Its call is a dog-like shrill yelp. It occupies large territory year after year. It has the usual courtship display of other eagles. This bird breeds mainly during January-March. The nest is a huge platform made of various sticks, on lofty trees like deodar, juniper, etc. or on stiff cliffs.

Status : The Himalayan Golden Eagle is becoming rare day by day, within the Indian limits. This is mainly due to destruction of its habitat, shortage in the food-availability, etc. This bird, therefore, can be considered as endangered.

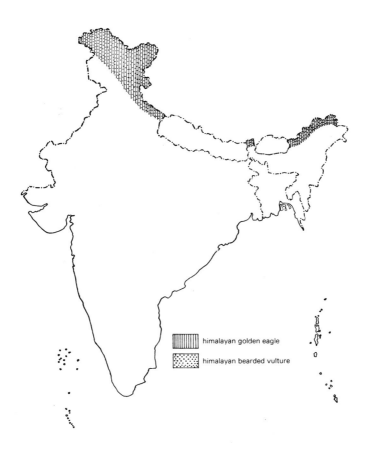

himalayan golden eagle

himalayan bearded vulture

155

himalayan golden eagle

HIMALAYAN BEARDED VULTURE

88. Gypaetus barbatus aureus (Hablizl) (E)

The Himalayan Bearded Vulture is an enormous eagle-like vulture with feathered head and neck, wedge-shaped tail and fully feathered legs. Its length is about 122 cm. The head and neck are creamy or rusty white, the rest of the upperparts being silvery grey and black with white streaks. The underparts are pale rusty white. The 'beard' is a tuft of bristle-like black feathers hanging from the chin. The sexes are alike. The immature bird is dark brown with nearly black head.

Distribution : The Himalayan Bearded Vulture is found in the mountains of southeastern Europe, islands in the Mediterranean Sea, east to northern China and south to southern Arabia, Pakistan, along the Himalaya east to Nepal, Bhutan and Arunachal Pradesh.

Habits and habitat : The Himalayan Bearded Vulture is an inhabitant of the high mountain ranges between c 1200 and 4000 m elevations. This bird has also been observed soaring at heights between 7200 and 7500 m. Its food consists of carrion including human corpses and offal. This vulture often feeds on refuse dumps in company with other vultures and ravens. It has a peculiar tendency of breaking long bones by dropping them and eating the marrow. It breeds from December to March and builds the nest in inaccessible places, often under a overhanging rock. It has an elaborate courtship display and both the sexes take part in incubation and bringing up of the young ones.

Status : The Himalayan Bearded Vulture is rarely seen these days in India. The immediate cause of its decimation is not precisely known. Possibly it has been ruthlessly killed in the past by the hill people who, irrespective of caste and creed, prize its meat highly. The Himalayan Bearded Vulture, therefore, should be considered as endangered.

OSPREY

89. Pandion haliaetus haliaetus (Linnaeus) (E)

The Osprey is a dark brown hawk of the size of a kite. Its length is about 56 cm. The head is brown and slightly tufted, with some white markings. There is a blackish band running backwards from behind the eye. The underparts are white with a conspicuous brown-streaked band across the upper breast. The lower surface of the toes is covered with sharp spicules to help in holding the slippery fish. Both the sexes are of the same colour but the female is larger. The immature bird has the feathers of the upperparts washed with white and the breast-band less defined.

Distribution : The Osprey breeds widely in the Palaearctic Region. It is mainly a winter visitor in southern Africa and the Indian subcontinent from Baluchistan east to Assam and Manipur, south to Kanyakumari, Sri Lanka, Maldive Islands and Andaman Islands from September to March. It possibly breeds also in the Himalaya between 2000 and 3300 m altitude (Ladakh, Kashmir, Garhwal, Kumaon) and Assam (Cachar)

Habits and habitat : The Osprey is almost invariably associated with water, either a river, a lake or the sea-coast. It is seen generally singly, perched on trees near the water from where it starts its fishing sorties — flying in wide circles over water, occasionally stopping in the mid-air like a kestrel to investigate any suspected movement of fish in the water below. Its food consists entirely of fish. Its nest is very large, built on trees, a crag, a boulder or even sometimes on the ground.

Status : The Osprey is rather scarce in India. In many localities the young birds do not survive to the fledgling stage as an after effect of feeding on fishes of pesticide-contaminated water. The population of the Osprey in India is, therefore, becoming rarer day by day, and as such, endangered.

osprey

SHAHIN FALCON

90. Falco peregrinus peregrinator Sundevall (E)

The Shahin Falcon is a broad-shouldered falcon with slaty upperparts, black head and nape, and conspicuous cheek-stripes. Its length varies between 38 and 46 cm. The throat and breast are pinkish white, the rest of the underparts being ferruginous, cross-barred with black from abdomen downwards. Both the sexes are of the same colour but the female is larger. The immature bird is more brownish black above and more ferruginous below.

Distribution : The Shahin Falcon is found in northern Pakistan, practically the entire Indian Union including the Nicobar Islands (Himalaya up to 2400 m altitude from Kashmir east to Arunachal Pradesh, south through the Peninsula to southern Kerala), excepting the arid and semi-arid areas of Rajasthan and Gujarat, also in Sri Lanka, Bangladesh and Burma east to southern Yangtze Valley in eastern China.

shahin falcon

Habits and habitat : The Shahin Falcon generally keeps to steep rugged hills. It also affects open country, thin jungle and cultivation. Its flight is extremely swift and direct, with a few rapid wing beats followed by a glide at a tremendous speed. It hunts mainly soon after dawn and in the afternoon well into the dusk. Its food consists mainly of birds like partridges, quails, pigeons, etc. It also eats parakeets, nightjars, bats, rats, mice, etc. Pairs of the Shahin Falcon occupy favourite crags year after year for nesting and for hunting over vast tracts. It breeds during March-May in the Himalaya and from January to April in the peninsular Indian hills. Its nest is a large and compact platform made of sticks, often with some inner lining. Being one of the most successful of hunting birds with its capacity to be tamed and trained easily, the Shahin Falcon is considered as the most prized falcon for the falconery.

Status : Large numbers of the Shahin Falcon are killed every year by man under the mistaken notion that it is a notorious poultry-lifter. Some birds are also caught for the falconers. The Shahin Falcon in India, therefore, should better be regarded as endangered.

Order Galliformes

NICOBAR MEGAPODE

91 **Megapodius freycinet** Gaimard (E)

The Nicobar Megapode is about the size of a domestic hen with conspicuously large feet and shorter tail. Its length is about 43 cm. The upperparts are rufescent brown with an olive wash. The head is ashy grey. The sides of the head have bare patches of red skin. The chin and throat are pale grey. The remainder of the underparts are greyish brown. The feet are provided with long and straight claws and the hindtoes are well-developed. The wings are shorter and rounded. Both the sexes are alike. The immature bird has the head rufescent brown. The chick is snuff brown in colour.

Distribution : The Nicobar Megapode is distributed in the Cocos Islands, (?) Little Andaman Island, the Nicobar group of Islands (excepting Choura and Car Nicobar), the Philippines, Sulawesi (Celebes), Lesser Sunda Islands, Moluccas to New Guinea and northern Australia.

Habits and habitat : The Nicobar Megapode is essentially a bird of the tropical moist dense forest along the sea-shores. It is generally seen in pairs, or in small parties or droves of adults, youngs and chicks. This bird is partly nocturnal and feeds in undergrowth like the jungle fowl. Its food consists of land snails, insects, worms and vegetable matter. It has no definite breeding season, but breeds almost throughout the year. The nest is a mound made of sand, leaves and other vegetable matter and is generally built in the forest near the beach. The mounds are 1.5 m high and 10 m or more in circumference. The number of eggs laid are variable and may be 20 in a single mound. No incubation is done by the hen, the heat generated by the decomposing vegetable matter helps incubating the eggs.

Status : The Nicobar Megapode was not uncommon in the Nicobar group of islands even in the first half of the present century. But collection of fresh eggs and random killing for flesh, especially by the recent settlers, have alarmingly reduced its population. This bird, therefore, is greatly endangered, at least within its Indian range of distribution, and needs effective protection.

nicobar megapode

PHEASANT-GROUSE

92. **Tetraophasis szechenyii** Madarasz (R)

The Pheasant-Grouse is a large pheasant-like bird of brownish colour. It is about 64 cm in length. The head has narrow streaks of black. The feathers of the lower back and rump are with narrow edges. The chin and throat are fawn coloured while the feathers of the underparts are edged and spotted with rusty. The outer tail-feathers have black and white tips. The female is similar to the male, but has no spur.

Distribution : The Pheasant-Grouse is found in southwestern China and eastern Tibet, extending just into the northeastern border of India in the Subansiri district of Arunachal Pradesh.

Habits and habitat : The Pheasant-Grouse is met with in the alpine zone between 3350 and 4600 m altitude, covered with fir and rhododendron. It moves about in small family parties of four to six, foraging among the scrub and short grassy vegetation. The food of the Pheasant-Grouse consists of roots, bulbs, tender shoots and green leaves. It is rather a less noisy bird with a characteristic loud and harsh voice. It breeds during the summer months.

Status : Within the Indian limits, the Pheasant-Grouse is a very rare bird.

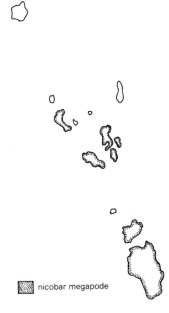

Nicobar Islands

nicobar megapode

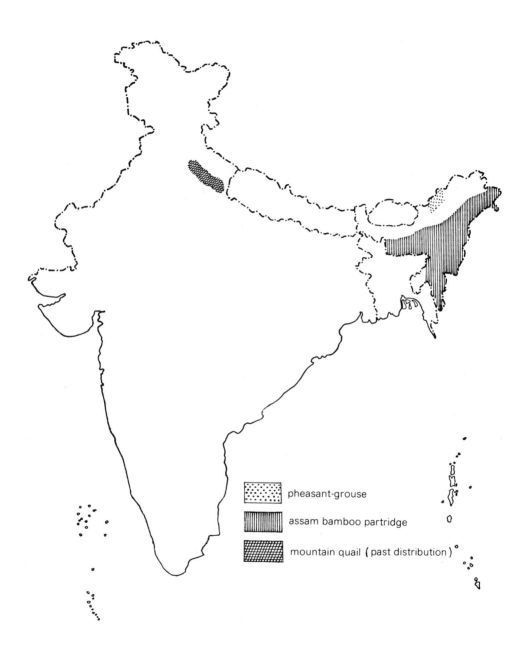

pheasant-grouse

assam bamboo partridge

mountain quail (past distribution)

163

ASSAM BAMBOO PARTRIDGE

93. Bambusicola fytchii hopkinsoni Godwin-Austen (R)

The Assam Bamboo Partridge is a rather long-tailed rufous-brown partridge with a broad rufescent white supercilium extending backwards to the nape, and a blackish line behind the eye, just below the supercilium. Its length is about 35 cm. The mantle is grey-brown, streaked and spotted with chestnut and black. The tail has brown and buff bars. The breast is chestnut with white and grey spots and streaks. The rest of the underparts are buff with large semilunar black spots, the spots being absent in the abdominal region. Both the sexes are similar in coloration.

Distribution : The Assam Bamboo Partridge is found in the hills of northeastern India south of the Brahmaputra river extending into Sylhet and Chittagong Hill Tracts of Bangladesh, and Chin Hills and Arakan Yomas of Burma.

Habits and habitat : The Assam Bamboo Partridge prefers open scrub jungles near cultivation in the foothills and adjoining plains. It also affects mixed scrub of willow, oak and tall grass along the banks of streams. This bird generally moves about in small family parties of five or six, foraging near streams, etc.,during the morning and evening hours. Its food consists chiefly of vegetable matter *e.g.* tender shoots, buds, berries, grains, seeds, etc. but it also takes insects like grasshoppers, termites, crickets, ants, etc., and grubs. Its flight is quite characteristic and clearly differs from that of other partridges found in the same habitat. It breeds chiefly from March to May.

Status : Even during the first quarter of the present century the Assam Bamboo Partridge was quite plentiful. But due to excessive hunting pressure coupled with destruction of its habitat in recent years, the population of this partridge has dwindled much. It is now rather a rare bird in India.

MOUNTAIN QUAIL

94. Ophrysia superciliosa (J. E. Gray) (Extinct)

The Mountain Quail is a rather long-tailed partridge, somewhat smaller than they Grey Partridge *(Fancolinus pondicerianus)*. Its length is about 25 cm. The sexes differ in colour. The male is a dark slaty olive-brown bird streaked with black, with a browner wash on the wings. The forehead is white and the supercilia are broad and white, being bounded both above and below by black patches. The face, chin and throat are black. A conspicuous broken band of white loops down from the cheeks to the sides of the throat. The under tail-feathers are black with white terminal bars. The bill is coral red in colour and the legs and feet dull red. The female is cinnamon-brown in colour, with narrow white supercilia. Its upperparts are streaked and spotted with triangular black spots, and the underparts are brownish with chestnut and black streaks. There is a black band on either side of the crown of head. The bill of the female is dusky red and its legs and feet are duller red. The immature bird is like the female.

Distribution : The Mountain Quail is known only from the Mussoorie and Naini Tal areas of western Himalaya.

Habits and habitat : The Mountain Quail was found in parties of five or six in grassland and bushes on steep hillsides between 1650 and 2100 m elevations. It was difficult to flush out for it was reluctant to fly. Its flight has been recorded as slow, heavy and short. Its food consisted mostly of grass seeds, but it probably also took berries and insects. It had a quail-like call while feeding but its alarm call has been stated to be like a short whistle, unlike that of any other quail.

mountain quail

Status : The Mountain Quail must have been extremely rare even when it was described in 1846. There are only ten specimens of this bird in different museums of the World. This bird was collected for the last time in 1876. Since then no authentic information about its existence is available. Ripley's (1952) report of a specimen being shot in eastern Kumaon needs confirmation. Therefore, for all practical purposes, the Mountain Quail is to be considered as extinct.

BLOOD PHEASANT

95.   Ithaginis cruentus (Hardwicke)   (V)

The Blood Pheasant is a large partridge-like bird of the size of a domestic fowl, with a grouse-like bill. Its length is about 46 cm. The sexes differ in colour. The male has the upperparts overall grey and the underparts apple green with whitish central streaks, and a mop-like crest. The naked orbital patch is bright red in colour and is bordered by black. The chin and throat are crimson. There are crimson splashes on the upper breast, wing shoulders, upper and under tail-coverts and the tail-feathers. The female is bright rufous-brown. Its throat is rufescent cinnamon, contrasting with the ashy grey crest and nape. The immature male is less brilliantly coloured.

blood pheasant

Distribution : The Blood Pheasant is distributed in the Himalaya and adjoining mountains from central Nepal east to Arunachal Pradesh, southeastern Tibet, and Yunnan, Szechuan and Sensi in China.

Habits and habitat : The Blood Pheasant is a bird of the higher elevations, occurring between 2500 and 4600 m altitude and moving up and down with the snow-line. It inhabits temperate and alpine forests of pine, dwarf rhododendron, ringal bamboo and juniper scrub. It is gregarious in habit and moves about in parties of five to 10, often up to 30 or more. It is a swift runner and runs uphill when disturbed. It feeds on moss, fern, pine shoot and lichen. Its call is long, high-pitched and somewhat kite-like. It breeds during April-May.

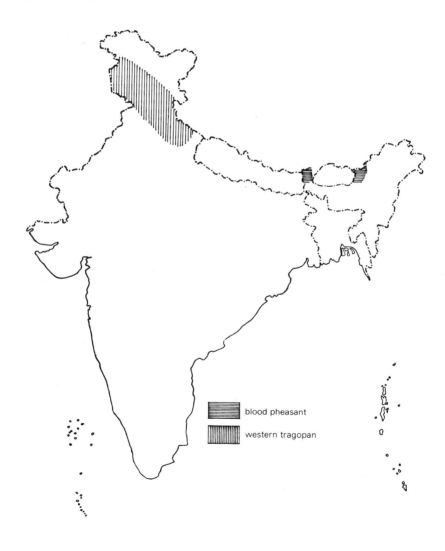

blood pheasant

western tragopan

Status : The Blood Pheasant is rather scarce. This beautiful bird is potentially vulnerable on account of its demand for menageries, destruction of its habitat and hunting chiefly for its ornamental plumage.

WESTERN TRAGOPAN

96. Tragopan melanocephalus (J. E. GRAY) (E)

Like all other tragopans, the male and the female of the Western Tragopan differ markedly in coloration. It is about 71 cm in length. In the male, the crown is black and has a red-tipped crest. The naked facial skin is bright red while the same on the throat is deep blue. The sides and back of the neck are red. The upperparts are finely vermiculated with buff-grey and black, and conspicuously marked with round white spots bordered with black. The foreneck and the upper breast are bright red. The rest of the underparts are blackish, marked with black-bordered, round, white spots and smeared with some amount of red. The female is a greyish bird with the head and neck tinged with rufous. The rest of the upperparts are streaked and spotted with black and white. The underparts are broadly streaked with white, the abdomen and flanks being paler. The immature male is like the female but has some black on the head and red on the neck.

Distribution : The Western Tragopan once occurred in the Himalaya from northern Pakistan east through Kashmir, Himachal Pradesh and Garhwal (possibly also Kumaon) in Uttar Pradesh.

Habits and habitat : The Western Tragopan generally inhabits thick undergrowth of ringal bamboo, etc., in hill forests between 1350 and 3600 m altitude. It moves about singly or in pairs, also in small family parties outside the breeding season. It is also known to feed in mixed feeding parties with other pheasants. Its food consists of vegetable matter *e.g.*,fresh leaves of oak, bamboo shoots, roots, fruits such as berries, acorns, etc., and insects. This tragopan roosts on the branches of trees during the night. Its alarm call has been rendered as *waa, waa, waa.* During the breeding season (June), the male is very much vocal. The nest is made of sticks with grass lining and is located either on the ground or in a tree.

Status : Over exploitation and destruction of the habitat in recent years have not only seriously reduced the population of the Western Tragopan, but also its distributional range. Within the Indian limits, it is now possibly localised in parts of Kashmir and Himachal Pradesh. This bird, therefore, should be considered as endangered.

western tragopan

SATYR TRAGOPAN

97. Tragopan satyra (Linnaeus) (R)

The Satyr Tragopan or the Crimson Horned Pheasant is a beautiful tragopan of orange-crimson colour, marked with round, black-bordered white spots. The male is about 68 cm in length. Its head and crest are black. There is a crimson streak on either side of the crest. The tail is black and the throat-patch is seminaked and blue. The female is smaller than the male and is rufous-brown in general colour. The tail is irregularly barred with black and buff. The young male is like the female but is less richly coloured.

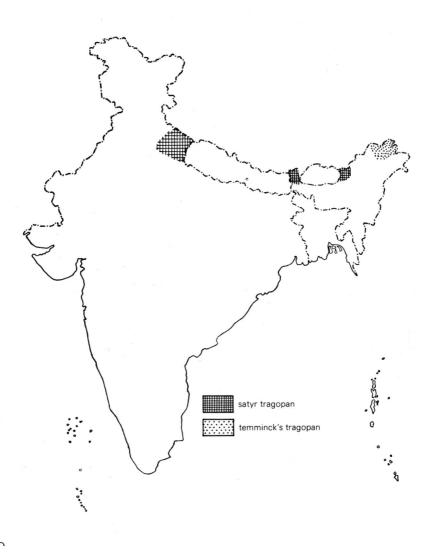

satyr tragopan

temminck's tragopan

satyr tragopan

Distribution : The Satyr Tragopan is found in the Himalaya from Garhwal (Uttar Pradesh) east to Bhutan and adjoining parts of Arunachal Pradesh and Assam.

Habits and habitat : The Satyr Tragopan inhabits forests of oak, deodar and rhododendron with some undergrowth on steep hillsides between 2400 and 4250 m elevation. It moves about in the forest digging for bulbs and roots which are its favourite food, but is also known to feed on leaves, shoots, tendrils, seeds, etc. Its call has been stated to be like the bleating of a kid. It breeds during the summer months.

Status : Due to destruction of habitat and indiscriminate hunting, the Satyr Tragopan has become rather rare in recent years.

BLYTH'S TRAGOPAN

98.   **Tragopan blythii** (Jerdon)   (R)

The male Blyth's Tragopan is a brilliantly red coloured tragopan with prominent white round spots on the back. Its length is about 68 cm. The anterior part of its head and the sides of the neck are black. The posterior part of the head, neck, anterior part of the back and the shoulder of the wing are bright crimson. The rest of the upperparts are brown, tinged with red and are marked with numerous smaller white and larger maroon spots. The bare facial and gular patches are yellow and are bordered by black feathers. The upper breast is crimson and the lower breast and abdomen are smoky grey. The upperparts of the female are blackish and are barred and bloched with black. Its underparts are browner. The immature male is more or less like the female.

Distribution : Blyth's Tragopan was previously found in eastern Bhutan and adjoining parts of Arunachal Pradesh east to Mishmi Hills and adjacent parts of southeastern Tibet; again, in the hill ranges of northeastern India south of the Brahmaputra river and northern and northwestern Burma.

Habits and habitat : Blyth's Tragopan is an inhabitant of the moist evergreen forest with thick undergrowth, between 1800 and 3000 m elevations. It moves about in small parties of four or five. Its food consists of vegetable matter such as buds, fruits, seeds, etc. Its call is a very fine sonorous *wak*, sometimes lengthened into *wa-ai-ai*. This tragopan breeds generally during April-May and makes rough and bulky nest of twigs and leaves in trees.

172

blyth's tragopan

blyth's tragopan

174

Status : Due to destruction of habitat and indiscriminate hunting, Blyth's Tragopan has become very rare. Recent reports indicate that within the limits of the Indian subcontinent, this tragopan is now to be found only in eastern Bhutan, Dafla Hills of Arunachal Pradesh and Nagaland.

TEMMINCK'S TRAGOPAN

99. Tragopan temminckii (J. E. Gray)   (R)

The male Temminck's Tragopan is a bright crimson coloured bird with circular, black-bordered, pearly grey spots on the upperparts. Its length is about 64 cm. The bare skin of the face and throat are cobalt-blue, while the head, borders of the face and a loop round the throat-patch are black. The underparts are marked with large triangular or diamond-shaped pearly grey spots. The flight-feathers are brown, mottled with buff and the tail is black. The female is greyish brown, mottled with blackish and with pale buff arrow-shaped markings. Its chin and throat are whitish marked with some black lines. The underparts are brownish with large whitish spots and black patches. The colour of the tail is like that of the back but has irregular blackish bars. The immature male is like the female but is larger, with black and red patches on the head and having some amount of red on the neck and upper-breast.

Distribution : Temminck's Tragopan is found in eastern Arunachal Pradesh (Mishmi Hills, northern Dibang and Tsangpo Valleys, etc.), northeastern Burma, southeastern Tibet and northern Yunnan, Szechuan, Shensi and Hupeh in China and extreme northwestern part of Tonkin (Vietnam).

Habits and habitat : Temminck's Tragopan is an inhabitant of cold and damp forests along sharp, wind-swept ridges and their slopes, with thick undergrowth and moss-covered trees, generally between 2100 and 3500 m elevations. It is solitary but is sometimes seen in groups of two or three. This tragopan is arboreal to a high degree. Its food consists mainly of vegetable matter.

Status : As a result of destruction of its habitat, Temminck's Tragopan has become rare in the Indian part of its distributional range.

175

temminck's tragopan

HIMALAYAN MONAL PHEASANT

100. *Lophophorus impejanus* (Latham) (E)

The Himalayan Monal Pheasant, more commonly known as the Monal, is a short and stout pheasant. It is otherwise called as the Impeyan. It is about 72 cm in length. The sexes differ in colour. The male is a brilliantly coloured bird with metallic sheen. Its head is bronze-green with a long crest

himalayan monal pheasant

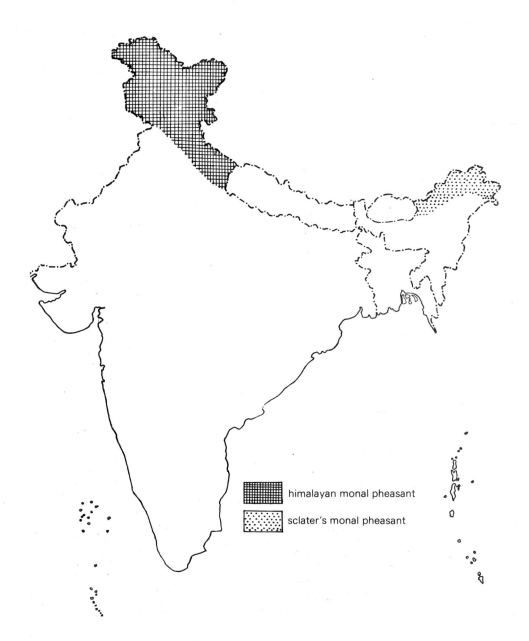

himalayan monal pheasant

sclater's monal pheasant

of wire-like shafts and spatula-tipped, metallic green feathers. The bare skin around the eye is blue while the throat and neck are purple blue and the mantle is bronze-green, purple and blue. There is a distinct white rump-patch. The tail is rufous, short, broad and square. The underparts are velvety black. The female is brown, mottled and streaked with darker and lighter brown. Its crest is shorter than that of the male and is composed of blackish, lanceolate feathers. The throat is white.

Distribution : The Himalayan Monal Pheasant occurs in eastern Afghanistan, northwestern Pakistan, Kashmir east along the Himalaya to Bhutan, and southeastern Tibet.

Habits and habitat : The Himalayan Monal Pheasant inhabits deodar, pine, oak, rhododendron and birch forests between 2600 and 5000 m elevations. It generally frequents open glades, pastures, hillside scrubs and grassy slopes. It is found singly, in pairs or in small parties. The Monal feeds on roots, tubers, bulbs and other vegetable matter and also on larvae of insects, worms, etc. Its call is like a ringing whistle. It breeds from April to June. The nest is a scrape in the ground under the shelter of a rock or a fallen tree-trunk.

Status : About a century back the Monal was not uncommon when thousands of them used to be exported to European countries. In the second and third decades of the present century the export to those countries fell to lots of hundreds only. This species is now very thinly populated in its range of distribution. It suffers heavy poaching especially in Himachal Pradesh during winter months when it descends to lower elevations. The Himalayan Monal Pheasant should, therefore, be considered as endangered.

SCLATER'S MONAL PHEASANT
101. **Lophophorus sclateri** Jerdon   (E)

Sclater's Monal Pheasant, otherwise known as the Mishimi Monal Pheasant, is very much like the Himalayan Monal Pheasant, but the male is duller and is without any distinct crest, the crown being covered with short, forwardly recurved blue-green feathers. Its length is about 72 cm. The white rump-patch is much more extensive and includes the upper tail-coverts. There is a broad band of white at the tip of the tail and another wide band of cinnamon at the base of it. The female is also similar to that of the Himalayan Monal Pheasant, but the rump and upper tail-coverts are pale greyish white. Its tail is black, marked with narrow whitish bars and is broadly tipped with white. The immature bird is like the female but has darker mantle and much paler rump and upper tail-coverts.

Distribution : Sclater's Monal is distributed in southeastern Tibet, most parts of Arunachal Pradesh, northern Burma, and Yunnan in China.

Habits and habitat : The Mishmi Monal Pheasant inhabits silver fir forest with dense rhododendron undergrowth between 3000 and 4000 m elevations. It occupies the same haunt day after day and is very noisy in the afternoon. Its food and call are similar to those of the Monal, but the call is rather distinct in tone. It is known to breed during May.

Status : Due to random destruction of its habitat and much hunting for its flesh, the population of Sclater's Monal Pheasant has dwindled in recent years. This bird, therefore, should be considered as endangered.

sclater's monal pheasant

ELWES'S EARED PHEASANT

102.   Crossoptilon crossoptilon harmani Elwes   (E)

Elwes's Eared Pheasant is a monal-sized pheasant with long, white ear-tufts which project like small horns behind the head. Its length is about 72 cm. The head is velvety black with deep scarlet patches of bare skin on the sides. A white ring encircles the nape, chin and throat. The upperparts are ashy grey, rather blackish on the neck and is paler on the rump and upper tail-coverts. The tail is metallic blue-black, glossed with green and purple and is laterally compressed. The longer central tail-feathers arch downwards. The underparts are ashy grey. The sexes are alike in coloration but the female is smaller. The chick is with velvety black head, dull black upperparts and dirty white underparts.

Distribution : Elwes's Eared Pheasant is a resident of northeastern Tibet extending to the northern fringes of Arunachal Pradesh, north of the main range.

elwes's eared pheasant

Habits and habitat : Elwes's Eared Pheasant inhabits grassy hill slopes and dwarf rhododendron thickets. between 3000 and 5000 m altitude, foraging in grassy clearings. It generally keeps in flocks of 5 to 10. It is rather reluctant to fly and usually runs uphill. This is a noisy bird and feeds mainly during the morning and evening hours. Its food consists mainly of vegetable matter *e.g.,* roots, tubers, shoots, fallen berries, seeds, etc., but it also takes insects and their larvae. It probably breeds during the summer months.

Status : Recent disturbances in the Indian part of its distributional range have caused the population of this pheasant to be scarce. Elwes's Eared Pheasant, therefore, is regarded as endangered, though it is protected near the monasteries.

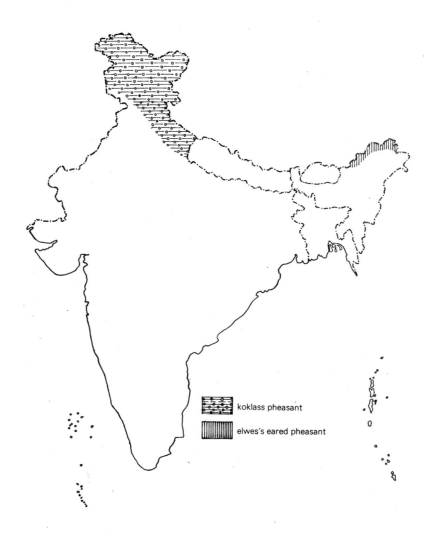

koklass pheasant

elwes's eared pheasant

KOKLASS PHEASANT

103. Pucrasia macrolopha (Lesson)   (E)

The Koklass Pheasant is a medium-sized pheasant with fully feathered head. It is about 61 cm in length. The sexes differ in colour. The head of the male is metallic green with a long brownish crest and two lateral, metallic green, horn-like ear-tufts. The upperparts are greyish and streaked with black. The underparts are largely chestnut. The female is mottled with black-and-brown, finely streaked with buff. Its crest is shorter and the ear-tufts are absent. The underparts are buffy and streaked with blackish.

Distribution : The Koklass Pheasant is distributed in the Himalaya from Afghanistan to central Nepal, then again discontinuously in northeastern Tibet and western China, north to southeastern Mongolia.

Habits and habitat : The Koklass Pheasant affects wooded ravines and steep hillsides in coniferous forest with scrub and ringal bamboo undergrowth, generally between 1000 and 4500 m elevations, but comes down to lower elevations during the winter months. It is generally seen singly or in pairs, but several of them can also be seen to feed on a particular hillside. It feeds

koklass pheasant

mostly on vegetable matter such as shoots, buds, fern leaves, tubers, berries, acorns, etc., but is also known to take insects. Its call has been rendered as *khwa-ka-kak*. This pheasant generally breeds from April to June. The nest is a scrape in the ground with a rough lining of sticks, leaves, grass, etc.

Status : The Koklass Pheasant is not a common bird these days. Destruction of its habitat and hunting for its flesh appear to be the main reasons for the decline of its population. This bird, therefore, is better regarded as endangered, at least in the Indian part of its distributional range.

CHEER PHEASANT

104. Catreus wallichi (Hardwicke) (E)

The Cheer Pheasant is a long-tailed pheasant, with a long, narrow and backwardly directed occipital crest of blackish brown, hair-like feathers. The length of the male varies from 90 to 118 cm. Its naked orbital skin is crimson. The upperparts are mostly buffy white and pale rusty, closely

cheer pheasant

barred with black. The tail is long and pointed, buffy grey and chestnut in colour and broadly barred with black and ashy grey. The underparts are buffy white and barred on the lower breast. The female is similar to the male in general effect but is smaller. Its underparts are more chestnut and the orbital patch is brick-red. The immature bird is more or less like the adult female but is duller, less conspicuously marked and does not have a crest.

Distribution : The Cheer Pheasant is found in northwestern Pakistan, Kashmir, Punjab, Himachal Pradesh, Garhwal and Kumaon in Uttar Pradesh east at least to west-central Nepal.

Habits and habitat : The Cheer Pheasant inhabits steep hillsides in oak forest covered with long grass and scrub, between 1400 and 3500 m elevations. It generally moves about in parties of five or six, actively digging

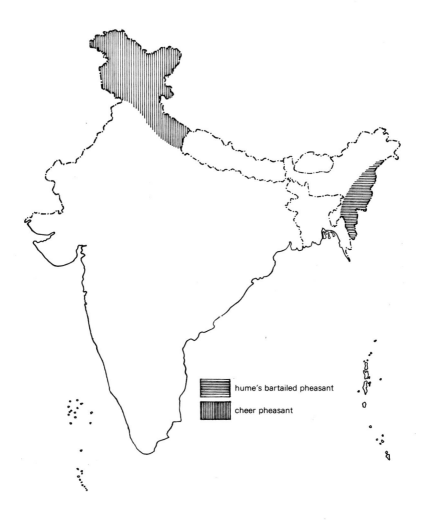

humé's bartailed pheasant

cheer pheasant

out roots and tubers which constitute its food. It also feeds on seeds, grains, insects, grubs, etc. The call is very loud and distinct, and has been rendered as *chir-a-pir, chir* and *chirwa* (each note repeated twice), and so on. It breeds from late April to early June. The nest is a depression in the ground, roughly lined with leaves and grass.

Status : The Cheer Pheasant was quite common even during the last century. But in recent years the entire Indian population has decreased seriously owing mainly to destruction of its habitat and hunting for flesh. This species is now considered as endangered.

HUME'S BARTAILED PHEASANT

105.   Syrmaticus humiae humiae (Hume)   (E)

Hume's Bartailed Pheasant is a long and straight-tailed pheasant like the Cheer Pheasant, but has no crest. The sexes differ in colour and size. The male is larger and is about 90 cm in length. The head, chin, throat and the neck of the male are glistening steel blue and the rump is with some white

hume's bartailed pheasant

markings. The bare facial skin is crimson. The back is somewhat golden coloured and scalloped with black. There are two broad white bars on the scapulars and two other narrow white bars on each of the wings. The tail is grey and has narrow chestnut and black transverse bands. The head of the female is reddish brown, and the crown is streaked with black, while the rest of the upperparts are chiefly sandy brown, streaked, barred and mottled with black. The bare patch of skin around the eye is much smaller. The tail is shorter and less pointed, chestnut-coloured, broadly barred with black and tipped with white. The underparts are lighter and the upper breast is spotted with black. The immature bird is like the adult female but is duller.

Distribution : The distribution of Hume's Bartailed Pheasant is patchy. It has been reported from Nagaland, Manipur, Mizoram and northern Burma west of the Irrawaddy river and south to Mt. Victoria.

Habits and habitat : Hume's Bartailed Pheasant inhabits mixed pine and oak forests with long grass and light undergrowth on steep hillsides, between 900 and 2000 m elevations. It moves about in pairs, in groups of three or in small family parties. Other habits of this bird are not known excepting that it produces a subdued, *buk buk* (repeated several times) note, and breeds during May-June.

Status : Hume's Bartailed Pheasant does not appear to have ever been common. Destruction of its habitat coupled with random hunting for flesh has made its population still thinner. As such, this bird should be regarded as endangered.

PEACOCK-PHEASANT

106. Polyplectron bicalcaratum (Linnaeus) (E)

The Peacock-Pheasant is a greyish brown pheasant of the size of a domestic hen, with a long tail and an erect crest of hair-like feathers. The length of the male is about 64 cm. Its head and back are brownish buff, the back spotted with white and the rump and upper tail-coverts are barred with whitish. The mantle, wing-coverts and the tail are marked with violet greenish blue ocelli with white rims, the ocelli being more elongated near the tips of the tail-feathers. The female is similar to the male in colour-pattern but is duller and smaller than the male and has a shorter tail. Its ocelli are obsolete on the shorter tail-feathers. The immature male is like the adult female.

peacock-pheasant

Distribution : The Peacock-Pheasant occurs in the hills and foothills of Sikkim, northern West Bengal, Bhutan, northeastern India, Bangladesh, Burma, Thailand, Laos, Vietnam and Hainan Island.

Habits and habitat : The Peacock-Pheasant inhabits dense evergreen forests from foothills to *c* 1200 m elevation. It moves about singly or in pairs. The food consists of grains, seeds, berries, figs, insects, grubs, snails and other small animals. Its usual call is a deep guttural *hoo* quickly repeated about seven times. It breeds from March to June. The male has a spectacular courtship display. The nest is a shallow depression in the ground, lined with some dry leaves.

Status : Due to destruction of much of its habitat and random killing for flesh, the Peacock-Pheasant has become much reduced in population-size. The bird, therefore, should be regarded as endangered, at least in the Indian part of its distributional range.

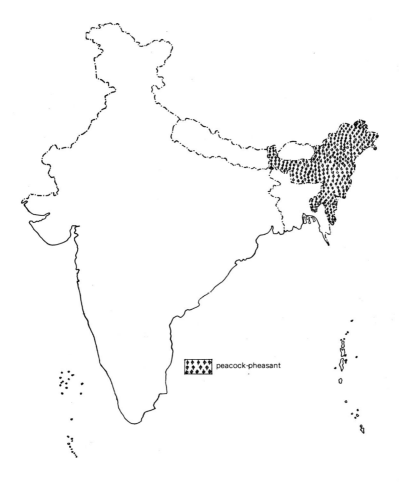

peacock-pheasant

INDIAN PEAFOWL

107.   **Pavo cristatus** Linnaeus

The Indian Peafowl is a colourful, swan-sized bird, with a small head bearing a fan-shaped crest of spatulatipped feathers, a white patch under the eye and a long, slender neck. The sexes are dimorphic. The male (cock) has a metallic bronze-green train of about 200 elongated feathers (upper tail-coverts), each of which is tipped with a purplish black-centred coppery disc. Its length (excluding the train) varies from 92 to 122 cm, while its total length (including the train) varies between 2 and 2.25 m. The neck and the breast are glistening blue in colour, while the lower back is bronze-green with some amount of black. A part of the wing is chestnut in colour. The female (hen) is brown and is slightly smaller than the male. It lacks the train. Its lower neck is metallic green and the breast is buffy brown with some wash of metallic green. Its wings have no chestnut-coloured feathers. The immature male is like the female.

Distribution : The Indian Peafowl is widely distributed in the Indian subcontinent from south and east of the Indus river, Jammu and Kashmir, east to Lakhimpur district in Assam, south to Mizoram and the whole of the Indian Peninsula. Extralimitally, it occurs in Chittagong Hill Tracts of Bangladesh, and Sri Lanka

indian peafowl

Habits and habitat : The Indian Peafowl is an inhabitant of dense scrub jungles and deciduous forests. It prefers to remain near some source of water. When disturbed, it runs away through the undergrowth, and flies while crossing a river. This bird roosts on the branches of trees. It is omnivorous. Its food consists of both vegetable matter (young shoots, fruits, seeds, etc.) and small animals (lizards, snakes, insects, and their larvae, etc.). During the non-breeding season the male and female move about in separate parties. The usual call is a loud and harsh *may-awe.* During the breeding season (January to October) a cock moves about with four or five hens. The male has an elaborate courtship display involving erecting and quivering of its train. Three to five pale cream-coloured eggs are laid in the nest which is a shallow scrape in the ground in a dense thicket.

Status : The peacock is the National bird of India. It is fully protected under the Wild Life (Protection) Act of India. In Rajasthan and Gujarat, this bird is not persecuted on religious grounds. Though often becomes a pest to agriculture, the peafowl is never molested on sentimental grounds also.

Order Gruiformes

BLACKNECKED CRANE

108. **Grus nigricollis** Przevalski   (E)

The Blacknecked Crane is a pale ashy grey crane with black head and neck. Its standing height is about 156 cm. The lores and the crown are bare and dull red in colour. There is a patch of white feathers behind and below each eye. The tail is covered by some drooping black plumes. The sexes are similar in coloration but the female is slightly smaller.

Distribution : The Blacknecked Crane is a breeding bird of central Asia from Ladakh to Koko-nor. It has been recorded as a winter visitor from Vietnam, Yunnan in China, Subansiri district of Arunachal Pradesh and Bhutan.

Habits and habitat : The Blacknecked Crane breeds on the shores of high altitude lake areas and swampy bogs between 4300 and 4600 m, but inhabits reed beds and open fallow paddyfields in their winter quarters. It feeds on fallen grains and probably also on roots, tubers, insects and small vertebrates. The call is more or less like that of the Sarus Crane *(Grus antigone)*, but has a higher pitch. It breeds during May-July. This bird has elaborate courtship display in which both the sexes take part. The nest is a huge and deep pad of vegetation, constructed on the ground.

Status : No information is available as to the exact population-size of the Blacknecked Crane. Reports from China which has the main breeding areas of this species, indicate its dwindled population. During recent surveys in Ladakh, Bhutan and Arunachal Pradesh, only a few breeding birds were seen in Ladakh, and a few small wintering flocks in isolated areas of Bhutan, and none in Subansiri district of Arunachal Pradesh. This species of crane may, therefore, be considered as endangered.

blacknecked crane

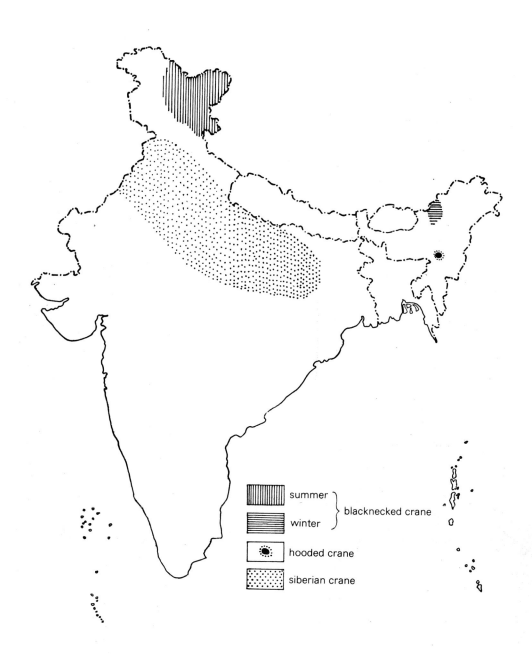

summer ⎱
        ⎰ blacknecked crane
winter

hooded crane

siberian crane

193

HOODED CRANE

109. Grus monacha Temminck (R)

The Hooded Crane is smaller than the Sarus Crane. Its standing height is about 90 cm. It is a dark slaty grey bird with a tone of brown, especially on the upperparts. Its head and about three-quarters of the neck are white, while the forecrown is red. The forecrown, forehead and the lores are overgrown with bristly feathers of black colour. The sexes are alike. The immature bird is pale grey with a black patch on either side of the whitish forehead.

Distribution : The Hooded Crane is essentially a Palaearctic species wintering in Japan and part of China. There is only one authentic record of its occurrence within the Indian limits (North Cachar; December, 1899). There are also two sight records of this species from Subansiri river, Arunachal Pradesh. Its alleged occurrence in Manipur as winter visitor is yet to be confirmed.

Habits and habitat : The Hooded Crane inhabits open plains and marshy areas in its wintering ground. It has been observed to move about in small parties. No specific data regarding the food, call, etc., of this bird are available, but presumably are similar to those of other cranes. No details of its breeding in the wild are available.

hooded crane

Status : The estimated population of the Hooded Crane is 5,500. However, for the potential disease risk due to too much concentration (about 75% of the total population) at the artificial feeding stations in Japan, the species is still considered as endangered. This crane has not been authentically recorded within the Indian limits for more than 80 years. The Hooded Crane, therefore, should be considered as extremely rare in India.

SIBERIAN CRANE

110.   Grus leucogeranus Pallas   (E)

The Siberian Crane or the Great White Crane is a snow-white bird of the size of a Common Crane *(Grus grus)*. Its standing height is about 140 cm. Its forehead, forecrown, face and the sides of the head have red bare skin with some white, bristle-like feathers. Some feathers of the wing are black which can be seen only when the bird is flying. The sexes are alike. The immature bird has cinnamon-buff feathers on the head and face, while the white feathers on other parts of the body are tinged with cinnamon-buff.

siberian crane

Distribution : The Siberian Crane is a breeding bird of northern Siberia, wintering in northern Iran, northern Pakistan, northern India and central China.

Habits and habitat : The Siberian Crane arrives in India (mainly northwestern Bihar, Payagpur jheel in Uttar Pradesh and Keoladeo Ghana National Park in Rajasthan) during late November and early December, and leaves India by the end of March to beginning of April. It is essentially a bird of the wetland and never moves away from the marshy areas. This crane moves about in family parties of three or four, or in small flocks of a dozen or so. It feeds exclusively on various parts of aquatic vegetation. While flying it forms a V-shaped arrangement. The call is a soft, musical *koonk-koonk.*

Status : The total world population of the Siberian Crane is about 190, besides 33 birds under captivity. This beautiful species of crane is, therefore, greatly endangered.

MASKED FINFOOT

111   Heliopais personata (G. R. Gray)   (R)

The Masked Finfoot is a cormorant-shaped water bird, more or less of the size of a domestic duck. Its length is about 56 cm. The sexes slightly differ in colour. In the male, the forecrown, face, chin, throat and the foreneck are velvety black and are bordered by a narrow white line. Its posterior crown and hindneck are steel-grey, and the dorsal and lateral aspects of the anterior part of its body are olive-brown in colour which gradually changes into light brown. The breast and abdomen are white and the tail is tipped with whitish. In the female, the throat and foreneck are white, surrounded by black, and the black frontal band is narrower than that of the male. The immature bird is like the female but the crown is not black and the area surrounding the throat is mottled with white.

Distribution : The Masked Finfoot occurs in Bangladesh, parts of the northeastern States of India adjoining Burma, Thailand, south through the Malaya Peninsula to Andalas (Sumatra).

Habits and habitat : The favourite haunt of the Masked Finfoot is a flooded depression in the forest surrounded by trees, canes and creepers. It is generally seen singly or in pairs. This bird is very shy and alert, and is a good runner and equally good swimmer and diver. It generally perches on tree-trunks overhanging the water. Its food consists of molluscs, crustaceans, insects, small fishes, vegetable matter, etc. Its call is a loud grunting quack. It breeds generally during July-August. Its nest is made of twigs placed on a horizontal branch of a tree in dense forest-swamp.

Status : There is no authentic record of the occurrence of the Masked Finfoot in India for more than half-a-century. This water bird, therefore, should be considered as exceedingly rare in India.

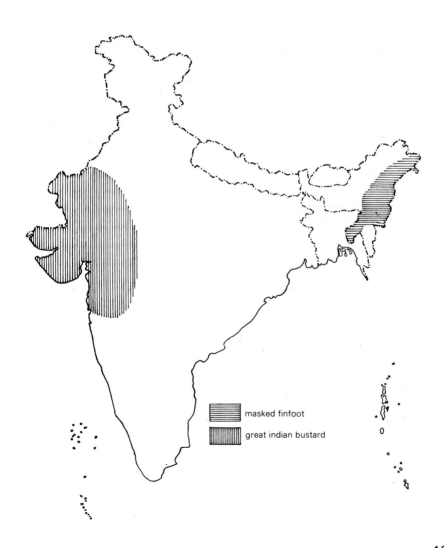

masked finfoot

great indian bustard

GREAT INDIAN BUSTARD

112.   *Ardeotis nigriceps* (Vigors)   (E)

The Great Indian Bustard is a huge ground bird with a long neck and long, bare legs, looking somewhat like a small ostrich. The male differs slightly from the female in size and coloration. Its standing height is more than a metre. The general colour of the male is deep sandy buff, finely vermiculated with black. The crown of the head is black and crested. Its underparts are white and there is a black band across the lower-breast. In the female, which is smaller than the male, the white areas of the head and neck are not pure white and the black breast-band is either rudimentary or absent. The immature male is like the female but has buff spots on the crown, hindneck and anterior part of the back.

Distribution : At present, the Great Indian Bustard is seen in the arid and semiarid areas of Rajasthan, Gujarat and Ahmadnagar district of Maharshtra. It is seasonally nomadic and is sporadically seen in suitable areas of western Madhya Pradesh and Karnataka.

great indian bustard

Habits and habitat : The Great Indian Bustard is an inhabitant of the open country having thorny bushes and tall grass intersparsed with cultivation This bird moves about singly, in pairs or in small to large parties of three or four to two dozens or more. This bustard is a very shy bird. When alarmed, it prefers to squat and freeze behind a bush than flying away. It is a good runner. It is omnivorous in diet. Insects, lizards, snakes, cereals, drupes and berries, tender shoots, etc., constitute its food. Its alarm call has been rendered as somewhat like *hook.* The breeding season is between March and September. The male is polygamous. The nest is constructed on the ground in which usually a single egg is laid, and only the female incubates.

Status : About a century ago, the Great Indian Bustard was widely distributed from the western districts of West Bengal, west to Pakistan (Sind and Punjab) and south to Tamil Nadu. But encroachment on its habitat for human needs and hunting for its flesh have curtailed not only its distributional range, but its numbers have also decreased alarmingly. The total number of this bird has been estimated as 745 only. This species, therefore, is greatly endangered.

BENGAL FLORICAN

113.   Eupodotis bengalensis bengalensis (Gmelin)   (E)

The Bengal Florican is a peahen-sized bird with long, bare legs. Its standing height is about 55 cm. The sexes differ in size and colour. The head, neck and the underparts of the male are velvety black. It has a moppy crest on the head and a bunch of plume-like feathers overhanging the breast, both of black colour. The dorsal parts are black, mottled and vermiculated with buff. The exposed part of the closed wing is white. The female is slightly larger than the male and is buffy in general coloration, vermiculated and mottled with black. It has neither a crest nor a white patch on the wing; instead, has a buff coronal streak on its dark brown head. The male in its first plumage is like the female.

Distribution : The distributional range of the Bengal Florican includes Brahmaputra Valley, Duars of Arunachal Pradesh and Assam, Duars and and Terai of Bhutan, West Bengal, Nepal and Kumaon, west to about Yamuna river. It is also reported from Comilla and Chittagong districts of Bangladesh.

Habits and habitat : The Bengal Florican is essentially an inhabitant of the grassland. It generally moves about singly. A number of individuals may, however, feed on the same patch of grassland. It feeds chiefly on insects, slugs, frogs, berries, grass seeds, etc., mostly during early morning and evening. When disturbed, it flies away to a distance of 100 to 300 m and then drops in the grass to hide. The alarm call has been recorded as a metallic *chik-chick-chick*. During the breeding season (March-April), coveys of four to eight consisting of both the sexes, are seen feeding in the same patch of grass. Its nest is a simple depression in the ground in which only two eggs are laid.

Status : The Bengal Florican has practically vanished from many parts of its former distributional range. It is now present in the sanctuaries on either side of the Brahmaputra river. The estimated population of this bird in Assam is about 300. The Bengal Florican is, therefore, greatly endangered.

bengal florican

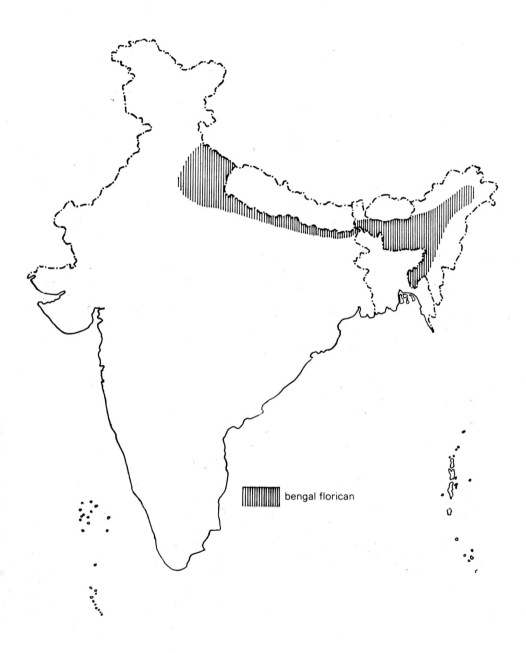

bengal florican

LESSER FLORICAN

114. Sypheotides indica (J. F. Miller)   (R)

The Lesser Florican or the Leekh is much like the Bengal Florican, but is somewhat smaller. It is about 46 cm in length. The male in the breeding plumage has the head, most parts of the neck and the underparts black. Its chin, centre of the throat and a broad band running down the sides of the lower neck are white. A patch on the exposed part of the closed wing is also white. The upper plumage is sandy buff, vermiculated and mottled with blackish. On either side of the head there are three tufts of black, spatulate feathers which project behind the head. The female is slightly larger than the male, sandy buff in colour, mottled with blackish, and has blackish arrowhead markings on the back. Two parallel blackish stripes run down the centre of the throat and foreneck. The forehead and crown are black with a pale median stripe. It has no head plumes. The male in the non-breeding plumage is like the female but has much white on the wings.

Distribution : The Lesser Florican is found in southern Pakistan and practically the whole of the Indian Union, excepting the very humid areas.

lesser florican

Habits and habitat : The Lesser Florican is an inhabitant of tall grass patches, scattered bushes and cultivated tracts. It frequents standing crops, especially those of cotton and millet. In habits it is much similar to the Bengal Florican but is less shy. It feeds mainly on insects,centipedes lizards, frogs and also on vegetable matter like shoots, grasses, herbs and fruits. The male emits a harsh, frog-like croak during the courtship display. This species breeds from July to September. Normally four eggs are laid in the nest which is a simple depression in the ground.

Status : Due to destruction of its habitat and hunting for its flesh, the Lesser Florican has become rare these days.

Order Charadriiformes

JERDON'S COURSER

115. **Cursorius bitorquatus** (Blyth)   (Extinct)

Jerdon's Courser or the Doublebanded Courser is a lapwing-like running bird having the upperparts pinkish sandy brown,with dark brown crown and hindneck. Its length is about 27 cm. A broad whitish supercilium passes from the lores to the nape. The chin and throat are whitish, the foreneck is

jerdon's courser

rufous, the breast and flanks are chestnut while the lower abdomen is greyish white. There are two white bands across the upper and lower breast. A white wing-bar and the black and white tail are characteristic. The leg is without a hindtoe. Jerdon's Courser can readily be distinguished from the Indian Courser *(Cursorius coromandelicus)* by its breast-bands and broad, white supercilium.

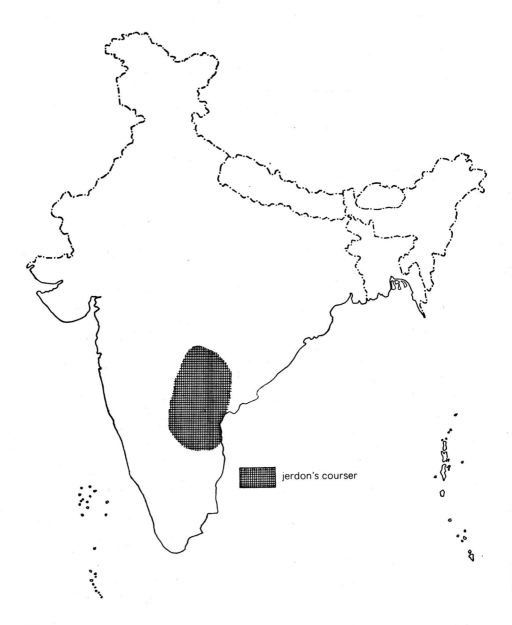

jerdon's courser

Distribution : Jerdon's Courser is known only from Godavari and Penner valleys (Nellore, Cuddapah, Sironcha, Bhadrachalam, Borgumpad and Anantapur areas) of Andhra Pradesh.

Habits and habitat : Jerdon's Courser inhabited thin forests and scrub jungles in the rocky ground in the river valleys. It was seen in pairs or in small parties. When alarmed, it either ran fast to take shelter under thick cover or took to wings. Its flight was more rapid than that of the Indian Courser. This bird was rather silent but occasionally uttered a plaintive cry. It was reported to lay a pair of eggs on the ground in scrub jungles.

Status : Since the discovery of Jerdon's Courser in 1848, it was only rarely recorded and not more than six skins are present in different collections. No specimen has been collected since 1871 and the last authentic sight record of it is in the year 1900, since then several thorough searches by competent ornithologists have failed to rediscover it. Jerdon's Courser therefore, seems to have become extinct.

INDIAN SKIMMER

116. **Rhyncops albicollis** Swainson (E)

The Indian Skimmer is a tern-like bird with a blackish brown upper plumage and white underparts. It is about 40 cm in length. Its forehead, the sides of the face and neck are white and the crown and nape are black. A dark stripe passes down the middle of the white rump and tail. The wings are long and pointed and the tail is slightly forked. The bill is orange-yellow, laterally compressed and knife-like, the lower mandible projecting well beyond the upper one. The leg is bright red. The sexes are similar in colour but the female is slightly smaller. The forehead of the immature bird is lighter brown and the tips of the tail-feathers are mottled with brown.

Distribution : The Indian Skimmer is found in Pakistan, India south to *c* 16°N latitude, Bangladesh, Burma and erstwhile Indochina.

Habits and habitat : The Indian Skimmer inhabits large rivers with sandbanks, estuaries and inshore coastal waters. It is generally seen in small flocks, skimming gracefully over the water, lightly ploughing the water surface with the projecting tip of the lower mandible. The food consists of small fish and tiny crustaceans. It feeds mostly during the day, but feeding during moonlit nights has also been reported. The call is a nasal *kap kap.* This bird breeds in mixed colonies with other terns on exposed sandbanks of larger rivers. Its breeding season is from middle of February to middle of April which, however, slightly varies with local conditions.

Status : Of late the Indian Skimmer has become scarce. Though the exact cause of this is not clearly understood, heavy pollution of the larger Indian rivers might possibly have played some role in dwindling its number. This bird, therefore, should be regarded as endangered.

Order Columbiformes

NICOBAR PIGEON

117. Caloenas nicobarica nicobarica (Linnaeus) (E)

The Nicobar Pigeon is a ground pigeon with a brilliant greenish lustre. It is about 41 cm in length. Its head, neck and upper-breast are dark slaty grey with metallic blue-green and copper-bronze sheen. The feathers of the hindneck are elongated and form glistening hackles. The flight-feathers are dark blue with green and purple metallic sheen. The tail-coverts and tail-feathers are white. The female is similar to the male but has the head, neck and breast more grey, and shorter neck-hackles. The immature bird is duller, lacks the neck-hackles and has a greenish tail.

Distribution : The Nicobar Pigeon is distributed in the Nicobar group of islands (Car Nicobar, Teressa, Camorta, Nancowry, Great Nicobar and others), South Andaman Island and Cocos Island. It is also found in the Mergui Archipelago eastwards through the Indonesian islands, Philippines and most of the islands of the Indo-Australasian region.

Habits and habitat : The Nicobar Pigeon is an inhabitant of the heavy evergreen forest. It is generally seen singly or in small parties, but at times in parties of 20 to 30. This pigeon freely moves about the forest floor, walking with wings drooping at the sides and pushing aside fallen leaves with the beak. The flight is swift and powerful. It is rather silent but occasionally utters a harsh guttural croak. The food consists of fruits and seeds fallen on the forest floor. It breeds possibly during January – April, like other pigeons. It nests in colonies. The nest is an untidy platform made of twigs and is built on trees three to eight metres above the ground. Only one egg is laid.

Status : Encroachment on the habitat of the Nicobar Pigeon and hunting for its flesh and as trophy have practically wiped it out from the Andamans, while in the Nicobar Islands too its position is precarious. The Nicobar Pigeon, therefore, is greatly endangered, at least in the Indian part of its distributional range.

nicobar pigeon

Andaman & Nicobar Islands

nicobar pigeon

Order Strigiformes

GREAT HORNED OWL

118. **Bubo bubo** (Linnaeus)   (E)

The Great Horned Owl or the Eagle-Owl is a large owl with dark brown streaks and tawny-buff mottlings. It is about 56 cm in length. Two prominent 'horns' or ear-tufts project above the head. The tarsus is fully feathered and the tail is moderately long and banded. There is a narrow blackish rim to the conspicuous facial disk. The eyes are yellow, large and forwardly directed. The chin and a patch on the throat are white. The rest of the underparts are fulvous-white. The breast has broad and bold black stripes and the upper abdomen has narrow stripes. The lower abdomen, under tail-coverts and the thighs have wavy brown bars. The sexes are alike. The Great Horned Owl can be distinguished from the Brown Fish Owl *(Bubo zeylonensis)* by its fully feathered tarsus and more erect ear-tufts.

Distribution : The Great Horned Owl is widely distributed throughout Europe, northern Africa, western Asia, Pakistan, the whole of Indian Union, Nepal, Bhutan, Bangladesh, south to Arakan in Burma.

Habits and habitat : The Great Horned Owl generally inhabits rocky hills, cliffs, ravines and well-wooded but open and cultivated country. It is often found near banks of rivers and streams. Though chiefly nocturnal, this owl has been seen active during the day-time also. The usual call is a deep, resounding *bu-bo*, the second syllable being much prolonged. It feeds chiefly on rats and mice but also takes birds, lizards, snakes, frogs, fishes, insects and crabs. It generally breeds from November to May, laying the eggs on the bare soil.

Status : This once-common useful (great destroyer of rats and mice in cultivated areas) bird is becoming scarcer day after day, mainly as a result of gradual destruction of its habitat and consequent shortage in its food-availability. The Eagle-Owl, therefore, should be considered as an endangered species, at least in India.

FOREST SPOTTED OWLET

119. **Athene blewitti** (Hume)   (R)

The Forest Spotted Owlet is largely similar to the commoner Spotted Owlet *(Athene brama),* but is slightly larger and has shorter wings and tail. Its length is about 23 cm. The head, nape, scapulars and the interscapulary region are dark brown and not spotted. There is an ill-defined collar of white spots on the hindneck and a strongly marked dark brown bar across the throat. The underparts are brownish and the breast has white fringes to the feathers. The forehead has some small spots. The tail has broad, white bands.

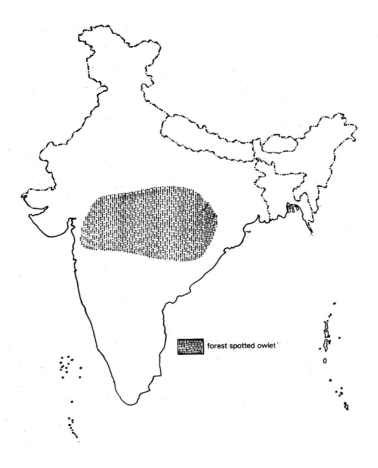

forest spotted owlet

Distribution : The Forest Spotted Owlet is known from peninsular India, ranging from Dangs district, Gujarat, south to erstwhile West Khandesh area of Maharashtra, east to eastern Madhya Pradesh and Sambalpur area of Orissa.

Habits and habitat : The Forest Spotted Owlet is a bird of the moist deciduous forest and groves of wild mango, but is also seen in the neighbourhood of streams. Practically nothing is known about its habits excepting that it is fairly diurnal and shy.

Status : The present status of the Forest Spotted Owlet is not clearly known. This species is known from only half-a-dozen specimens preserved in different collections, the last one being taken in October, 1914 at Mandvi, Surat district, Gujarat. Recent attempts by competent ornithologists to locate this bird in Orissa and elsewhere have failed. But a photograph taken in 1968, supposedly of this species, tentatively confirms its existence. The Forest Spotted Owlet should, therefore, be considered as extremely rare.

Order Caprimulgiformes

CEYLON FROGMOUTH

120. Batrachostomus moniliger Blyth (R)

The Ceylon Frogmouth is a night jar-like bird of the size of a myna, with a very wide gape and broad, swollen bill. Its size is about 23 cm. The sexes slightly differ in colour. The male is a greyish brown bird, vermiculated and mottled with white, buff, black and chestnut. Its head is spotted with black having white margin. There is a band of white on the hindneck. The female is dull rufous in colour. The immature bird is barred with brown.

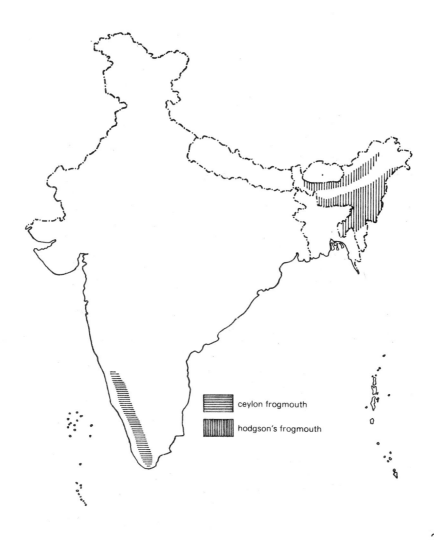

ceylon frogmouth

hodgson's frogmouth

Distribution : The Ceylon Frogmouth is distributed over the southern rain forest tracts of Western Ghats from North Kanara district of Karnataka, south to Trivandrum district of Kerala and Sri Lanka.

Habits and habitat : The Ceylon Frogmouth is an inhabitant of dense evergreen forest and secondary jungles. It is nocturnal in habit and spends the day perched across a branch in a tilted posture. It is reported to feed on moths, beetles and grasshoppers. It breeds mainly during January-April, in India. The nest is constructed on the fork of a tree or on a horizontal branch with moss, lichen and bark. Generally a single egg is laid.

Status : The Ceylon Frogmouth is a rare bird, at least in the Indian part of its distributional range.

HODGSON'S FROGMOUTH

121. **Batrachostomus hodgsoni hodgsoni** (G. R. Gray) (R)

Hodgson's Frogmouth is very similar to the Ceylon Frogmouth, but does not have white spots on the wing-coverts. Instead, it has broad white patches on the scapulars. It is about 27 cm in length. The immature bird is like the female, but is duller and has bars of blackish brown all over the body.

Distribution : Hodgson's Frogmouth is found in Sikkim, Bhutan, Arunachal Pradesh, and the hills south of the Brahmaputra river in the northeastern States of India, extending to Bangladesh and northern Burma.

Habits and habitat : Hodgson's Frogmouth is an inhabitant of the dense subtropical evergreen forest. In habits also, it is very similar to the Ceylon Frogmouth. As usual, it is nocturnal and very difficult to locate because of its coloration. Its breeding season is from April to July. Its nest is also like that of the preceeding form. As a rule, two eggs are laid.

Status : Like the Ceylon Frogmouth, Hodgson's Frogmouth is also a rare bird.

Order Coraciiformes
ASSAM BROWNBACKED HORNBILL
122. Ptilolaemus tickelli austeni (Jerdon) (R)

The Assam Brownbacked Hornbill is a medium-sized hornbill, slightly larger than a kite. The sexes slightly differ in size and coloration. The male is about 76 cm in length and is dark brown above and bright rufous below. Its cheeks, throat and the sides of the neck are white, and the foreneck is light rufous. The central tail-feathers are brown, but the rest of the tail-feathers are black with broad, black tips. The bill is surmounted by a small, sharp-edged, yellowish casque. The female is smaller than the male. The sides of its neck are of the same colour as that of the crown. Its underparts are more brown and less rufous.

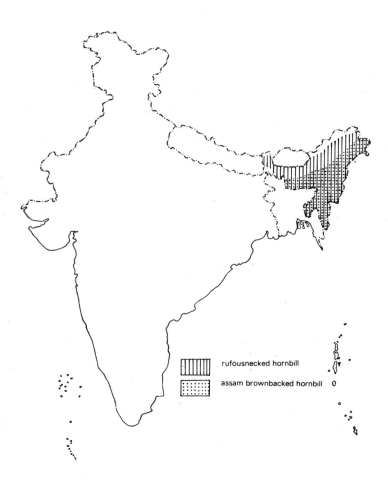

rufousnecked hornbill

assam brownbacked hornbill

Distribution : The Assam Brownbacked Hornbill is found in the hills south of the Brahmaputra and Luhit rivers.

Habits and habitat : The Assam Brownbacked Hornbill is an inhabitant of the evergreen forest, from the plains to 1000 m altitude. This bird generally moves about in flocks of 8 to 10 individuals, but may also form larger flocks of 20 or more. It is very noisy and restless and feeds chiefly on fruits like wild figs, drupes, berries, etc., but also takes insects, lizards and other small animals. The call consists of croaks, chuckles and squeals. This hornbill breeds mainly during April-June. The nest is a hollow in a tree, four to nine metres above the ground.

Status : The Assam Brownbacked Hornbill was found in good numbers half-a-century ago, but now has become rare. Deforestation resulting in non-availability of suitable nesting trees, hunting for the alleged medicinal values of its flesh, fat, bones and casque and the use of the latter two as charm by tribal people, appears to be the main reasons for its dwindled population.

RUFOUSNECKED HORNBILL

123. **Aceros nipalensis** (Hodgson) (R)

The Rufousnecked Hornbill is a large hornbill of the size of a vulture. Its length is about 122 cm. The sexes differ in colour. The head, neck and breast, in the male, are rufous while its abdomen is maroon. The dorsal parts of the body are black, glossed with dark green. The terminal half of the tail-feathers as also a patch near the tip of each wing are white. The bill is horn-shaped, yellow in colour and has vertical, blackish ridges on the sides of the upper mandible. The naked patches of skin on the cheeks, chin and the throat are scarlet, and those around the eyes are blue. The female is but slightly smaller than the male, and is black. It, however, has the white wing and white tail-tips of the male. The immature bird has a smaller bill which has no lateral ridges.

Distribution : The Rufousnecked Hornbill is distributed in the sub-Himalaya from Nepal, east to Arunachal Pradesh and the hills south of the Brahmaputra river in the northeastern States of India, extending to Bangladesh, Burma, Thailand and erstwhile Indochina.

rufousnecked hornbill

Habits and habitat : The Rufousnecked Hornbill is a resident of the evergreen and deciduous forests with tall trees. It is primarily an arboreal bird, keeping in pairs or in small flocks of four or five, on branches of trees, though it occasionally descends to the ground to feed. It is rather a noisy bird emitting a variety of loud roars, croaks and cackles. Like other hornbills, this bird is essentially frugivorous. It takes larger drupes and berries, fruits of nutmeg, etc. It breeds during the months of April and May. The nest is made in a natural hollow of a lofty tree-trunk.

Status : The Rufousnecked Hornbill, though rather common in some protected areas, has become rare in many parts of its distributional range, for the reasons mentioned under the Assam Brownbacked Hornbill.

ASSAM WREATHED HORNBILL

124. **Rhyticeros undulatus ticehursti** Deignan   (R)

The Assam Wreathed Hornbill is a large hornbill with an entirely white tail. The sexes differ mainly in colour. In the male whose length is about 114 cm, the head, excepting the sides, is deep chestnut which gradually changes to black on the hindneck. The sides of the head and and foreneck are buffy white. Other parts of the body are glossy black. The bill is horn-shaped, pale yellow in colour and is provided with transverse ridges at the base of both the mandibles. The female is slightly smaller and is entirely black, excepting the tail which is white, as in the male.

Distribution : The Assam Wreathed Hornbill is found in the Duars and foothills of eastern India, hills south of the Brahmaputra river, extending to Bangladesh, Burma, Thailand, erstwhile Indochina and Malay Peninsula.

Habits and habitat : The Assam Wreathed Hornbill is an inhabitant of the tropical evergreen forest from the plains to 2400 m altitude. This bird has a characteristic noisy flight. It feeds on large drupes and berries, wild figs, lizards, other small animals, etc. The male utters a grunt. The breeding season is chiefly during April-May. A natural hollow in a lofty tree-trunk is used to lay the eggs.

Status : The Assam Wreathed Hornbill was quite common during the past three or four decades, but now has become rare everywhere for reasons given under the Assam Brownbacked Hornbill. This bird is also much sought after for its feathers for the tribal headgear.

assam wreathed hornbill

assam wreathed hornbill

NARCONDAM HORNBILL

125.   Rhyticeros (plicatus) narcondami (Hume)   (V)

The Narcondam Hornbill is like the Assam Wreathed Hornbill in plumage pattern, but is smaller in size, being only slightly larger than a kite. It is about 66 cm in length. The head and neck of the male is rufous. Its throat is slightly paler than the head. The tail is white, and the rest of the plumage is black, glossed with dark green. The female is black excepting the tail which is white like that of the male.

Distribution : The Narcondam Hornbill is restricted to the Narcondam Island in the Bay of Bengal.

Habits and habitat : The Narcondam Hornbill is a bird of the tropical rain forest. It is found in small flocks of three or four, sitting in a single tall tree. This bird is noisy and fearless. It feeds exclusively on wild figs. The flight is heavy and slow. The call has been recorded as *ka-ka-ka-ka-ka* with the tone quality of a domestic fowl's cackle.

Status : The population of the Narcondam Hornbill was estimated in 1905 as 200, all confined to an area of less than 5 sq km. A sruvey of 1969 reports this bird as still plentiful. Nevertheless, in view of its endemic nature, and that too in a small island, the Narcondam Hornbill is to be regarded as vulnerable.

narcondam hornbill

INDIAN PIED HORNBILL

126. Anthracoceros malabaricus malabaricus Gmelin   (R)

The Indian Pied Hornbill is a large, black and white hornbill, slightly smaller than a vulture. It is about 89 cm in length. The upperparts of the male are black, glossed with green and the underparts are white. The outer tail-feathers are black but have white tips. The bill is large, wax-yellow in colour with some patches of black, and is surmounted by a high, ridge-like casque whose anterior end is pointed. The casque is convex on the sides and has a patch of black. The female is slightly smaller than the male and has a different colour pattern on its bill.

Distribution : The Indian Pied Hornbill has a wide distributional range covering the Himalayan foothills from Punjab, east to Bhutan, northeastern States of India West Bengal, Bihar, Orissa, eastern parts of Madhya Pradesh and Andhra Pradesh. It also occurs in Bangladesh and extreme northern portion of Burma.

indian pied hornbill

Habits and habitat : The Indian Pied Hornbill is an inhabitant of the moist deciduous and evergreen forests, often invading groves of large mango trees. This bird is mainly arboreal in habit and is found in small parties of 4 to 10 individuals. It also feeds on the ground. The call has been rendered as *kak-kak, kak-kak.* The food consists chiefly of fruits like wild figs, drupes, berries, etc. It also takes fishes, lizards, snakes, nestling birds and other small animals. It breeds principally during the months of April and May. The nest is a natural hollow in a tall tree-trunk.

Status : In recent years, the Indian Pied Hornbill has become rare for the reasons stated under the Assam Brownbacked Hornbill.

MALABAR PIED HORNBILL

127. Anthracoceros coronatus coronatus (Boddaert) (R)

The Malabar Pied Hornbill is a large black and white hornbill slightly smaller than a vulture. It is about 92 cm in length. The tips of the flight feathers, the whole of the outer tail-feathers and the underparts in the male,

malabar pied hornbill

are white, the rest of the plumage is black, glossed with green. The bill is large, wax-yellow in general colour with some patch of black at the base and surmounted by a high ridge-like casque which ends in front in a single point. Its iris is orange red and the bare orbital skin is blue-black. The female is slightly smaller in size, has the plumage coloration of the male, but its iris is brown and the bare orbital skin is fleshy white.

Distribution : The Malabar Pied Hornbill is found in the Chota Nagpur Plateau in Bihar and adjacent areas of West Bengal and Orissa, Andhra Pradesh, Madhya Pradesh, foot of the Western Ghats from Ratnagiri south to Kerala. It also occurs in Sri Lanka.

Habits and habitat : The Malabar Pied Hornbill is an inhabitant of the evergreen and moist deciduous forests. It often congregates around fruiting trees in forest villages. This bird feeds mainly on fruits like wild figs, drupes, berries, etc., but also takes termites. The call has been recorded as *kak-kak, kak-kak*. The breeding season of this hornbill in peninsular India is chiefly during March-April. The nest is a hollow in a tree-trunk.

Status : The population of the Malabar Pied Hornbill has dwindled much for the reasons mentioned under the Assam Brownbacked Hornbill.

GREAT PIED HORNBILL

128. Buceros bicornis homrai Hodgson (R)

The Great Pied Hornbill is a large, black and white hornbill of the size of a vulture. The sexes slightly differ in size. The male is about 130 cm in length. Its face, back and the underparts are black, while the neck, lower abdomen and the tail along with its coverts are white. The wing has two white bands, and the tail has a broad, sub-terminal band of black. The bill is horn-shaped and is surmounted by a large, U-shaped casque which is concave on the top. The female is similar to the male in plumage coloration, but is slightly smaller.

Distribution : The Great Pied Hornbill has a discontinuous distribution. It occurs in the Western Ghats from Khandala in Maharashtra south to Kerala. The other population is found in the lower Himalaya from Nepal east to Arunachal Pradesh, other northeastern States of India extending to Bangladesh.

Habits and habitat : The Great Pied Hornbill is an inhabitant of the moist deciduous and evergreen forests, from the plains to about 1500 m altitude. This bird is very wary and difficult to approach. Its flight is labored and noisy. Like most other hornbills, it takes mainly fruits (drupes, berries, wild figs, etc.)

great pied hornbill

great pied hornbill

but also takes lizards, snakes, nestling birds and rats. The call is a very loud *tok* which is repeated several times. It breeds during March-April in the northern and northeastern areas of its distribution and from February to April in southwestern India. The nest is a natural hollow in a lofty tree-trunk.

Status : The Great Pied Hornbill has become rare for the reasons stated under the Assam Brownbacked Hornbill.

224

REPTILES
&
AMPHIBIANS

Order Testudines

LEATHERBACK TURTLE

129. Dermochelys coriacea (Linnaeus) (R)

The Leatherback is the largest species of the living turtles of the World. Its carapace-length varies between 140 and 180 cm. Its average weight is about 400 kg and the maximum recorded is 725 kg. The species is devoid of all cornified epidermal structures. It has no scute on the carapace or on the plastron and no scale on the skin; the jaws are devoid of flattened horny plates. The carapace is smooth-skinned and rubber-like and has a number of longitudinal ridges which provide it considerable rigidity. Its body is somewhat triangular in shape. There is no sharp angle between the carapace and the plastron. Its head is large, the neck massive, the lower jaw bears a median hook and the upper jaw a pair of strong cusps flanked by deep notches. The limbs are paddle-shaped and clawless. The anterior pair of flippers are triangular and extremely long and enlarged. The hind flippers are broad and are connected to the tail by folds of skin. The carapace is slaty black with white spots; ventral coloration is variable and is generally a mixture of pink, white and black. Sometimes the spots have a pink or bluish tinge. In mature females, the crown of the head has a pink spot. The tail is black.

leatherback turtle

Distribution : The Leatherback is found in the warmer and temperate waters of the Atlantic, Pacific and Indian Oceans.

Habits and habitat : This turtle is mainly a pelagic species, usually found in open seas. It is highly migratory. It feeds on large marine invertebrates including jelly-fishes, small to medium-sized fishes and marine plants. It breeds three or four times in a year but the peak period is during May and June. The nesting period is from March to July in the Northern and from October to February in the Southern Hemisphere. Nesting takes place by night and an individual may nest as many as nine times in a season, at intervals of about 10 days. 90-200 eggs are deposited at a time in a 60-100 cm deep pit on a sandy beach. Several clutches are laid during a year. The female turtle ploughs considerable area around the egg-deposition spot, so as to confuse the predator of the exact location of the egg clutches. The incubation period varies from 60 to 70 days.

Status : The status of this species is indeterminate, but is rare.

TORTOISESHELL TURTLE

130. *Eretmochelys imbricata* (Linnaeus) (R)

The Tortoiseshell Turtle or Hawksbill is the smallest of the marine turtles. Its carapace is narrow and strongly serrated behind; in the juvenile it is covered with horny plates, with a dark mottling. The general outline of the carapace is cordate and it elongates with the age of the turtle. The scutes on its shield are thicker and strongly overlapping; four pairs of inframarginal scutes are present. Its head is very narrow, with distinct scales over it, and the snout tapers to a point. The bill is like that of a bird, with ridged jaws. Hawksbill is generally about a metre in length. The adult weighs between 60 and 120 kg; the heaviest recorded so far is 140 kg. The limbs are two-clawed. The carapace is amber coloured, with radiating brown and black streaks on the scutes. The plastron varies from yellow to orange (reddish brown) in colour. Many individuals are dark brown to black with yellow blotches.

Distribution : This turtle is found in the warmer waters of the western Atlantic Ocean, northward to Massachusetts in U.S.A. and southward to southern Brazil, Indian and Indo-Chinese waters. It has been recorded from coasts of southern Japan, Mexico, Central America, northern South America, Madagascar, Sri Lanka and India, especially Andaman and Nicobar groups of Islands.

228

Habits and habitat : The Hawksbill frequents coastal waters including shallow vegetated bottoms as well as bays and lagoons with muddy bottoms, lacking extensive beds of submerged vegetation. It propels with its front flippers. The hindfeet are mainly used for steering and for excavation of the nest. Its food mainly consists of sponges, coelenterates, ectoprocts, echinoderms, gastropod and bivalve molluscs, barnacles, crustaceans, ascidians and fishes. Sometimes its diet is supplemented by marine plants. The breeding season extends from November to February with peak in December-January. Nesting takes place generally by night and the female turtle walks about extensively on the sand bank before selecting a site for the nest. After the nest is ready, the mother turtle lays 96-127 eggs in a clutch during the day. The incubation period varies from 50 to 65 days.

Status : This species is endangered in many areas of its range where it is killed in large numbers for the horny shields.or keratin layer of its shell. This layer is much thickened and exhibits remarkably beautiful yellow brown translucence, when removed from the shell by heating. Keratin layer thus obtained is used for adornment and for making fashionable toilet articles and furniture.

tortoiseshell turtle

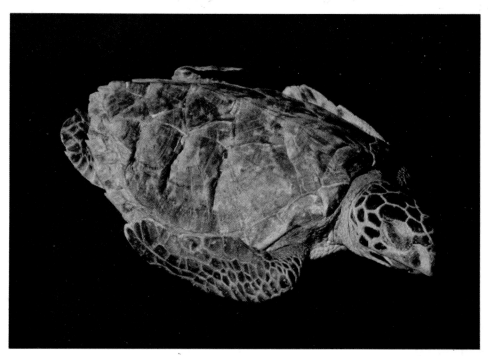

GREEN SEA TURTLE
131. Chelonia mydas (Linnaeus)   (E)

The Green Sea Turtle is the largest of the hard-shelled species of marine turtles and is considered to be the most valuable reptile of the World. This turtle has a flat, stream-lined, heart-shaped, smooth body. Its carapace is never completely ossified. Its head is round and small in comparison to the body, the snout short, the beak not hooked and edges of the jaws smooth. It has a pair of prefrontal shields and four pairs of more or less juxtaposed scutes. Neither its head nor legs can be pulled under the shell. The flippers are long. The carapace is dark blue-black in the hatchlings, and green, olive, brown, buff or black in the adult. The underside is white in the hatchlings and pale yellow in the adult. The colour of the head and flippers is like that of its shell but the edges of the head scales are pale. The carapace in the adult turtle reaches up to 105 cm in length. The turtle normally attains a weight of 150-175 kg; the heaviest recorded is of 425 kg.

Distribution : This species is found in all the tropical and subtropical oceans of the World. It also occurs in the Mediterranean Sea but does not breed there. It is common in the vicinity of the Andaman Islands.

green sea turtle

230

Habits and habitat : The Green Sea Turtle frequents inshore waters, less than 25 m in depth and sheltered by reefs. The normal mode of progression both in water and on land involves simultaneous sweeps of the front flippers. It feeds on submerged marine algae and seaweeds. It migrates great distances for food and breeding. Its mating season is from May to July. Suitable sandy beaches are used for breeding. Female turtles usually congregate in large numbers on such beaches mainly between June and November to lay eggs. The female turtle digs roughly a 60 cm deep hole in the sand, and 350-600 eggs are laid therein, usually during the early part of the night. After egg laying, the mother turtle fills the hole with sand and returns to the sea. Its incubation period is 40-52 days.

Status : Due to excessive exploitation of this turtle for flesh, cartilage and eggs, its population has alarmingly dwindled throughout the World. This turtle is an important food source of people inhabiting the sea-shores and islands. Its cartilage is processed to make turtle soup, which is regarded as a delicacy. Societies have been set up all over the World to protect this turtle and its nesting grounds. These societies are also engaged in hatching the turtle-eggs by artificial incubation, and ultimately releasing them to the natural habitat.

OLIVE RIDLEY TURTLE

132. Lepidochelys olivacea (Eschscholtz) (R)

The Olive Ridley Turtle is a small, broad and flattened marine turtle, whose carapace-length varies between 65 and 72 cm. A fully grown female at the time of breeding ranges from 40 to 55 kg in weight. Its head is large and triangular in shape and individual bones do not become completely fused until late in life. The coastal scutes are 6-9 on each side, the central scutes 8-9 and the marginal ones 12 pairs; the mid-marginals are much wider; a single nuchal and a pair of supracaudals are present. The plastron consists of paired gular, humeral, pectoral, abdominal, femoral and anal scutes. The intergular may be single, double or even absent. There are four pairs of inframarginal scutes. The orbits are distinctly large. The limbs are provided with one or two claws. The carapace is olive grey, the top of the head grey-brown, the shields yellow-white, the plastron creamy-yellow and the edges of the flippers light yellow-brown.

Distribution : The Olive Ridley is widely distributed in the tropical waters of the Pacific, Indian and South Atlantic Oceans. The main nesting localities of this species in India are on the east coast (Digha in West Bengal and Orissa) and Andaman Islands.

Habits and habitat : It is found in coastal waters as well as in the open sea. Its food consists of small crustaceans (shrimps and crabs), molluscs, jelly-fishes, fishes, and marine algae. The breeding season is from September to March. The female lays 90-135 eggs in a clutch in India and Sri Lanka. The incubation period ranges between 49 and 62 days.

Status : The number of this turtle has declined considerably in recent years on account of extreme predation of its eggs, and the slaughter of nesting adults for flesh by man.

olive ridley turtle

olive ridley turtle

BATAGUR

133. **Batagur baska** (Gray)   (E)

The Batagur is a moderately large, web-footed, aquatic species of terrapin, reaching to a length of 61 cm when fully mature. The species is characterised by the presence of a denticulated middle ridge in both the upper and the lower jaws. The front feet are provided with four claws. The carapace is smooth, heavy and moderately depressed. In the young an interrupted vertebral keel is present, which disappears in the adult. The nuchal shields are broader than long; the second and the third vertebrals are subequal; the plastron is much smaller than the shell opening, laterally angulate in the young and rounded in the adult, truncated anteriorly and notched posteriorly; the lingual shield is larger than the axillary. The head is comparatively smaller with an upturned, pointed and strongly projecting snout. Its shell is uniformly brown, olive-brown or greenish; the head and the undersurface of the neck are brown. In the breeding season, the male assumes a brilliant coloration, the nostrils becoming pale blue, the head deep black, and the neck and front limbs deep crimson. The hind part of the Batagur remains dull reddish purple and eyes greenish yellow throughout its life.

Distribution : This terrapin is recorded from southern West Bengal in India, Bangladesh, Burma, Thailand, Vietnam, Malay Peninsula and Sumatra.

Habits and habitat : The Batagur is found in fresh, brackish or even salt waters. It occurs in freshwater lakes, canals or other water bodies. But its most favourite habitat is the shallow, muddy, tidal regions at the wide river mouths, lined with mangrove or other vegetation. The Batagur is an omnivorous terrapin but prefers a vegetarian diet consisting of stems, leaves and fruits of riverside plants; it also feeds on molluscs, crustaceans, and fishes. It mates from September to November. It nests in a colony on

batagur

batagur

sandy banks from the beginning of January to early March. In a season, the female lays 50-60 eggs in three clutches (generally 10-30 eggs in each clutch). The interval of egg-laying varies from 15 to 20 days. The incubation period under natural conditions ranges between 80 and 100 days.

Status : This species is endangered over much of its range, on account of heavy exploitation of its eggs and adults for food, and habitat destruction. This species was over-exploited in Bengal in the mid-nineteenth century and its fat was much used for the manufacture of soap in Calcutta.

Order Crocodylia

GHARIAL

134. Gavialis gangeticus (Gmelin) (E)

The Gharial is a large, slender-snouted, fish-eating, amphibious crocodile, adult males reaching around 6.5 m and the females about 4.5 m in length. The body is strongly armoured with scutes. More than two dozens sharp pointed teeth are present on each side of the upper and lower jaws. The adult is olive in colour and the young lighter, spotted or barred with dark brown. The adult male bears a tough bulbous excrescence at the tip of the snout, resembling an earthen pitcher or 'Ghara', hence the name. When the male emerges out of the water, it produces a hissing sound.

Distribution : This species is found in Bangladesh, India, Nepal and Pakistan. It is mainly restricted to the Indus, Ganga, Mahanadi and Brahmaputra rivers and their tributaries.

gharial

Habits and habitat : The Gharial prefers to live in deep fast-flowing water, high banks, deep pools and undisturbed sand banks at the river-edge for nesting and basking. It basks on the sand banks for long periods during the winter when the water level is low. It feeds mainly on fishes, but occasionally on birds, goats, dogs and other vertebrates. Sometimes it attacks human beings also. Nesting takes place from late March to mid-April on sand banks on the river-edge, or in mid-river islands. Between 18 and 40 elliptical eggs (85-90 mm long and 65-70 mm wide) are laid in deep nests. Incubation period ranges from 83 to 94 days. The female guards the nest-site and also closely attends the hatchlings for several months. Sexual maturity is attained between 8 and 12 years of age, when it reaches a length of about 3 metres.

Status : At present, the status of the Gharial is endangered. It is mainly due to disturbance in its habitat, and killing of the animals for skin. In addition, its eggs and hatchlings are heavily predated by fishes, monitor lizards, birds of prey and carnivores. Its eggs are not spared even by tribals.

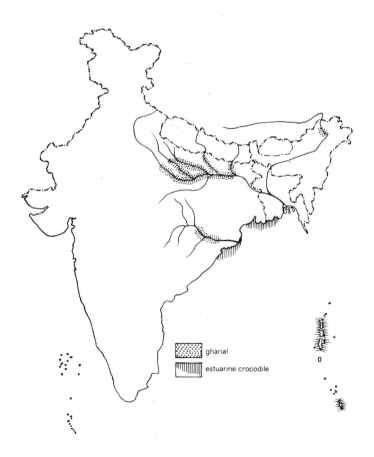

gharial

estuarine crocodile

In the nineteenth and early twentieth centuries, the Gharial was in abundance in many areas, but is now extinct or extremely depleted in number throughout its former range. It is almost extinct in Bangladesh and Pakistan, where even less than 20 individuals are left in each country. The estimated Indian population was about 75 animals in 1970 and the species was almost on the verge of extinction. But recently implemented conservation measures gave it a new lease of life in India. Now, its number has increased to about 500 individuals (including the juveniles), distributed in major rivers of Uttar Pradesh, Madhya Pradesh, Orissa and Assam. In addition, there are about 1800 individuals in captivity.

ESTUARINE CROCODILE

135. Crocodylus porosus Schneider   (E)

The Estuarine Crocodile is the largest of all the existing crocodiles. Its length ranges from 7 to 8 m, the maximum recorded is around 10 m. The body is shielded by an overall armature of closely set, horn-sheathed, bony plates, with saw-toothed fringes along the upper border of the tail. The adult is dark olive and the young is pale, with large black spots. The muzzle is about twice as long as its breadth at the base and tapers to a point. The jaws bear formidable pivoted teeth, less than 20 on each side. The teeth remain exposed even when the mouth is closed. The fourth tooth on each side of the lower jaw is enlarged and fits into a notch on the side of the upper jaw.

Distribution : This species has a wide range of distribution and is found on the east coast of India and the Andaman and Nicobar Islands. Extralimitally, it occurs in Sri Lanka, Bangladesh, east to the Philippines, the western Caroline Islands (Palau Group), Malaysia, Indonesia, Brunei to Papua New Guinea, the Soloman Islands, Vanuatu and northern Australia. Formerly, it was available near Cochin in India but now it has disappeared from that area.

Habits and habitat : The Estuarine Crocodile is a sluggish and lethargic creature, typically associated with brackish waters, such as the coastal mangrove swamps, estuaries, etc., but also visits freshwater rivers and grassy swamps. It is well-adapted to semiaquatic mode of life. It appears like a dead log on land, lying in wait for the quarry which are generally domestic animals; in water it is an expert fisher. Although it lives in saline water, it drinks fresh water. This crocodile is mostly a shallow water feeder. The juvenile and the subadult eat mainly crustaceans, insects and small fishes. The adult takes an increasing proportion of vertebrate diet, like fishes, reptiles, water birds and small mammals. It does not even spare

238

human beings. Sexual maturity in male is attained at the age of 16 years (3.2 m length) and in the female in 10 years (2.2 m length). This crocodile makes a mound-like nest on a sloping bank in the wet season and lays between 25 and 120 eggs. The incubation period is between 80 and 100 days. The female remains near the nest and defends it most carefully. She assists the hatchlings to leave the nest, carries them to water and remains near them for a considerable period.

Status : This crocodile is threatened throughout the World on account of its extensive hunting for hide and for its habitat destruction. The commercial value of its leather is the main reason of its over-exploitation. As a result, it has become quite rare in the coastal regions of southern India. Remnants of it are now confined to the estuaries of the Ganga and Mahanadi, and coastal regions of West Bengal, Orissa and the Andaman and Nicobar Islands. The total Indian population of this species is between 170 and 330. Several breeding centres in Andhra Pradesh, Tamil Nadu, Orissa and West Bengal are successfully rearing this species. It breeds readily in captivity.

estuarine crocodile

MUGGER

136. Crocodylus palustris (Lesson) (E)

The Mugger is much smaller than the Estuarine Crocodile or the Gharial in size. It is 3-5 m in length. Its snout is short and broad. The adult is dark olive and the juvenile pale, with black spots. The muzzle is about 1.50-1.75 times as long as broad at the base. The dermal armour is quite similar to that of the Estuarine Crocodile. The upper jaw has 19 teeth and the lower jaw 14-15 on each side.

Distribution : The range of distribution of this species includes Iran, Pakistan, India, Bangladesh, Nepal and Sri Lanka. The Marsh Crocodile is found in scattered populations all over India, except in the States of Jammu and Kashmir, Himachal Pradesh, Punjab and the northwestern desert region. Its easternmost limit of distribution is Arunachal Pradesh.

Habits and habitat : This sluggish crocodile occurs in any kind of freshwater habitat, and is occasionally reported in brackish waters, well within the tidal limits. It prefers still waters, having a depth of 3-5 m and may

mugger

be present in rivers, streams, jungle-pools, man-made lakes, village-ponds and large irrigation reservoirs. It avoids fast flowing rivers during the monsoon period. Like other crocodiles, the mugger is also carnivorous. Hatchlings predominantly feed on aquatic insects and fish-fingerlings and the adults feed on fishes, frogs, birds, and small mammals. The breeding season is from November to February in India. Males exhibit a strong dominance hierarchy and the dominant male mates with several females. Mating takes place in water. The female starts digging trial nest pits at least a fortnight before the actual egg-laying. The nest is made inside a burrow. The nest chamber is a wide-mouthed pitcher-shaped structure, dug quite away from the edge of water in a high sloping bank. The egg laying takes place between late February and first week of April, and 10-35 eggs are laid in a clutch. The incubation period varies from 50 to 65 days. Hatchlings which are ready to emerge make grunting noise from within the nest, stimulating the mother crocodile to excavate the nest and carry them to water. Hatchlings are from 25 to 30 cm in length and weigh about 60 to 100 g.

Status : In India, the main threats to the survival of the mugger are (i) hunting for its hide and medicinal value of its body parts, (ii) consumption of its eggs by human beings and carnivores, (iii) predation of its hatchlings by birds like herons and storks, (iv) natural calamities like the flood and desiccation, and (v) its habitat destruction.

Population of this crocodile has depleted considerably throughout its range, and the present population-size is estimated to be around 5,000 in India. The best known populations are in Tamil Nadu (400) and Gujarat (200). More than 2000 eggs are collected every year by different State Crocodile Breeding Centres in India for captive hatching and rearing for eventual release in the natural habitat.

Order Squamata

WATER MONITOR

137. *Varanus salvator* (Laurenti) (E)

The Water Monitor is the second largest of all the monitors of the World, attaining a length of about 3 m, including the tail. Like other monitors, it has a tapering head and long, slender neck. Its ear-openings are distinct. The eyes are provided with lids and have round pupils. The nostrils are round or oval and are situated at the anterior end of the head. Its teeth are long, sharp recurved, and laterally flattened and are frequently replaced. The tongue is very long, forked anteriorly and protrusible. Its tail is long strongly compressed and powerful. The body is covered with small overlapping granular scales. A fully grown lizard is dark olive, indistinctly spotted with yellow; the young is blackish, with small yellow and large rounded spots arranged in transverse rows.

Distribution : This species is distributed throughout the Indian subcontinent, including the Andaman and Nicobar groups of Islands. Elsewhere it is found in Sri Lanka, Bangladesh, northern Burma, southeast Asia and northern Australia.

Habits and habitat : The Water Monitor inhabits wet, marshy, humid forests, banks of rivers, estuarine forests, etc. It is more aquatic than other species of monitors. It can swim far off in the sea in search of food. It is omnivorous in diet but has special liking for birds' eggs and fishes. It breeds from June to August. 15-30 eggs are laid in holes on the river-banks or on trees beside water.

Status : This species is severely depleted in number and is at risk almost throughout its range of occurrence. The skin of this monitor makes excellent leather. From 1930 till recently, about 20,000,000 skins of the Indian Water Monitor have been shipped from Calcutta alone. Its skin is in heavy demand in Europe. However, this lizard is protected under Schedule I of the Indian Wildlife (Protection) Act, 1972.

water monitor

COMMON INDIAN MONITOR

138.   Varanus bengalensis (Daudin)   (E)

The Common Indian Monitor is a medium-sized, dark brown monitor. It is popularly known as *ghorpad*. It measures from 72 to 75 cm in the head and body length. The young possesses pale ring-spots and blackish cross-bars. The blackish cross-bars sometimes also persist in the adult. The tail is very strong, long and compressed, and measures about 100 cm in length. Characteristically, the scales on the crown are larger than those on the neck region and those of the anterior part are rounded and keeled posteriorly. The snout is convex terminally. The nostrils are oblique slits lying midway between the eye and the end of the muzzle. The teeth are acute, long, sharp and recurved. The tongue is very long, forked and protrusible.

Distribution : The Common Indian Monitor occurs throughout the Indian subcontinent.

Habits and habitat : This monitor is mostly diurnal. It is found in variable habitats, such as, forest, desert, river bank, by the side of nullah, marshy land, tidal creek and the sea coast. It occupies burrows, dense clump of vegetation, hollows of trees, cracks and crevices. This monitor is

common indian monitor

graceful in its movement and is a good climber and swimmer. It is a formidable reptile, bites hard, lashing with the tail and scratching vigorously with its powerful claws, when approached or caught in the wild condition. Its main food items are small terrestrial vertebrates, preferring ground-birds and their eggs; also takes arthropods and fishes. It breeds from July to September. The eggs, 19 to 30 in a clutch, are deposited in holes and are covered with leaves, rubbish and sand.

Status : The population of the Common Indian Monitor has alarmingly dwindled throughout the country, due to excessive exploitation of the adults for their commercially valuable skins.

YELLOW MONITOR

139. **Varanus flavescens** (Gray)   (E)

The Yellow Monitor is of dark brown colour with a reddish tinge on the body. It measures about 36 cm in the head and body length. The tail is strongly compressed and is about 46 cm in length. The snout is short and convex, and the nostrils are oblique slits. The scales on the crown are smaller than the nuchal ones, and the dorsal scales are strongly keeled. The digits are very short.

yellow monitor

Distribution : It is known from northern India from Punjab to West Bengal.

Habits and habitat : It is a very good swimmer and prefers to make burrows on muddy bunds around ponds, lakes and canals. The freshwater crabs and small fishes are its main food items. The breeding season is from July to August. It lays about 20 eggs in a clutch. The eggs are deposited in holes on the banks of ponds, lakes and canals.

Status : The population of the Yellow Monitor has greatly run down, as it has been exploited commercially for its beautiful skin.

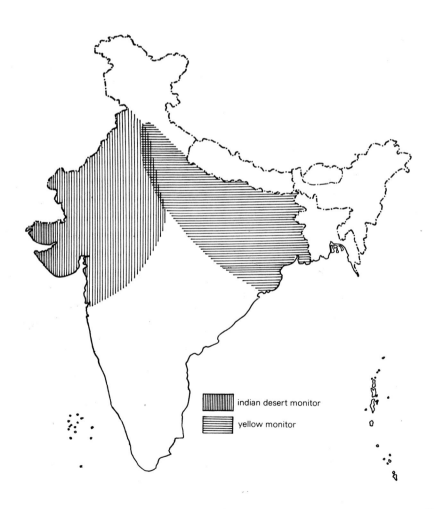

indian desert monitor

yellow monitor

INDIAN DESERT MONITOR

140. *Varanus griseus* (Daudin) (E)

The Indian Desert Monitor is sandy, brownish yellow or occasionally greenish yellow in colour, heavily speckled with dark grey or greyish brown. It measures about 52 cm in the head and body length and about 80 cm in the length of tail. The body is sometimes cross-barred with brown, especially on the tail; the young is spotted with yellow. The snout is depressed at the end. The nostrils are oblique slits, lying much nearer to the eyes than the end of the muzzle. The digits are moderately elongated. The tail is rounded and whip-like. The scales on the crown are usually larger than the nuchal scales. The dorsal scales are obtusely keeled, and the lateral caudal scales are indistinctly keeled.

Distribution : It occurs in the drier parts of Madhya Pradesh, Maharashtra, Rajasthan and Punjab in India. Extralimitally, it extends to Pakistan, Afghanistan, Iran and north Africa.

Habits and habitat : This monitor lives in burrows in undulating sandy grounds, with sparse vegetation. It can attain great speed in its movement, if required. During quick movements, however, the body remains raised above

indian desert monitor

the ground. Its food mainly consists of locusts, grasshoppers and crickets; it also takes small vertebrates. The number of eggs in a clutch varies from 15 to 20, and they are kept buried in the sand till hatching.

Status : Like other monitors, it is hunted extensively for its valuable skin. Its population has, therefore, become exceedingly low.

INDIAN ROCK PYTHON

141. **Python molurus** (Linnaeus) (R)

The Indian Rock Python is the second largest and heftiest of the Indian snakes. Its length ranges from 2.5 to 4.5 m; the maximum recorded length is 7 m and weight 85 kg. The head is distinct from the neck and has symmetrical shields; the rostral, the anterior supralabials, and the anterior

indian python

and posterior infralabials are pitted. Its eyes have vertical pupils. The scales on the body are smooth and are arranged in 60-75 rows. The tail is rather short. The colour of the body varies from pale grey to yellow above, and is yellow below; the flanks are paler. A dorsal series of large walnut-coloured crown saddles alternate with pinkish laterals.

Distribution : This species is distributed in India, Bangladesh, Pakistan, and Sri Lanka.

Habits and habitat : This python inhabits marshes, gallery forests and wet rocky areas near streams and pools. It occupies burrows, dense clumps of vegetation, large rotten logs, caves, crevices and ruins. It is a good climber and at times, suspends itself from the branch of a tree, waiting motionless for a prey to come within its reach. It is extremely fond of water and is an expert swimmer. It hibernates in winter into hollows of trees, underneath rocks or in rock-shelves. It is more nocturnal than diurnal. Its food largely comprises reptiles, birds and mammals. It is oviparous and exhibits parental care. The mother python coils herself round the egg-clutch, which consists of 60 to 100 eggs, till they hatch.

Status : The population of the Indian Rock Python has declined to an alarming level during the last fifty years, due to illegal international trade in its skin which are in high demand in the World market. Except for its protection in sanctuaries and national parks, it has become extremely rare elsewhere. It is however, protected under Schedule I of the Indian Wildlife (Protection) Act, 1972, and under Appendix I of the CITIES.

RETICULATED PYTHON

142. **Python reticulatus** (Schneider) (E)

The Reticulated Python is the largest and heaviest of all the Indian snakes. It attains a length of about 10 m; the young at birth, measures 60-75 cm. In most of the characters, it resembles the Indian Rock Python. The body colour is light brown or yellowish above, with dorsal series of large, dark brown, circular or rhomboidal spots, often confluent with each other. Each spot is edged with black and yellow. It is whitish or yellowish below.

reticulated python

Distribution : This python is distributed throughout northeastern India and through Burma to southeastern Asia; also found in Nicobar Islands.

Habits and habitat : The Reticulated Python inhabits the wet evergreen forest and is semiaquatic. Its food consists of small mammals, birds and reptiles occasionally medium-sized mammals like wild boar, deer, cattle, and even man become its prey. It lays eggs in a large clutch, up to 100 in number. Parental care is extended by the female python till the eggs are hatched.

indian eggeating snake

reticulated python

Status : This is the most threatened species amongst snakes. In southeast Asia, roughly 1,85,700 pythons were killed ruthlessly during 1958-1964 for their skins.

INDIAN EGGEATING SNAKE

143. Elachistodon westermanni Reinhardt (R)

The Indian Eggeating Snake apparently looks like a cat-snake but has the fearful appearance of a krait. It measures about 80 cm from tip of the snout to vent and the tail is nearly 13 cm. The body is laterally compressed, and there is no clear demarcation between the head and the neck. The general coloration is olive. The head is spotted and with yellow stripes from rostral region to neck running above the eyes; also, some black stripes run from the angle of the eye to the neck region.

Distribution : This snake is known from Mal and Baradighi in Jalpaiguri district of West Bengal, Purnea in Bihar, Rangpur in northern Bangladesh and Chitawan district in southeastern Nepal. Lately, it has also been recorded from the Corbett National Park in Uttar Pradesh.

indian eggeating snake

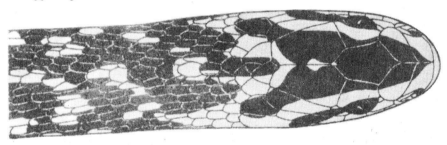

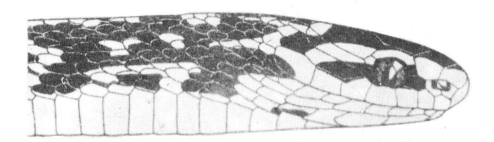

Habits and habitat : This snake occurs in moist deciduous tropical forests. It is non-aggressive and wary. Its main food item is the eggs of birds; it also takes other organisms.

Status : Nothing is known about the status of this snake. However, from very poor collection-records, it appears to be a rare animal.

Order Urodela

HIMALAYAN NEWT

144. **Tylototriton verrucosus** Anderson   (E)

The Himalayan Newt is a dark brown Indian salamander having a long tubercular body, depressed head, two pairs of limbs and a vertically flattened tail which is as long as the head and body or a little longer. Mid-dorsal vertebral ridge and cranial ridges on the head are quite prominent and well-

himalayan newt

developed. Two rows of knob-like porous glands, one on either side of the vertebral ridge, are present. Each row has 14-18 glands. This is the only species of salamander so far recorded from India.

Distribution : The Himalayan Newt has so far been recorded from West Bengal (Darjeeling district), Sikkim, Arunachal Pradesh (Lohit district) and Manipur in India. Elsewhere this salamander is available in Nepal, Burma, Thailand and western China.

Habits and habitat : This Newt is quite rare and is found in both seasonal and perennial pools in certain hilly pockets of the eastern Himalaya. Various localities have been recorded in Darjeeling district of West Bengal, on altitudes between 1260 and 2220 m. Adults congregate in pools after one or two pre-monsoon showers during April-May for breeding. Hibernation takes place in late October. Its food consists mainly of aquatic vegetation, insect-larvae, tadpoles and earthworms.

Status : On account of urbanisation this species is becoming rare throughout its range and needs strict protection. Hence its status is endangered now.

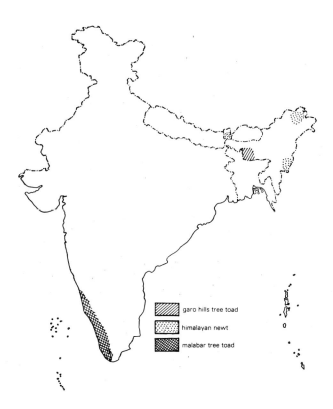

garo hills tree toad
himalayan newt
malabar tree toad

Order Anura

MALABAR TREE TOAD

145. **Nectophryne tuberculosa** (Günther)   (I)

The Malabar Tree Toad is small toad with webbed toes. The tips of the fingers and the toes are dilated into truncated discs. It measures 3.5-4 cm from the head to vent. The colour is brownish grey above. A white band is present from below the eye to the shoulder and another on the flank. The underside is whitish, with some black spots. The tympanum in this species is distinct. The parotids are present, but less developed. The fingers are webbed at the base and the first finger is half the length of the second. The skin of the back is tubercular; the largest tubercles are arranged in two rows on the sides of the back.

Distribution : This species is so far known from the Malabar area, Kerala.

Habits and habitat : Nothing in particular is known about the habits and habitat of this species. However, it is endemic to heavy rainfall areas. An allied species in Malaysia has been observed on bushes and small trees near water during the breeding season, and the eggs are laid in strings.

Status : Nothing definite is known about the status of this species, except that it is poorly represented in most of the collections.

GARO HILLS TREE TOAD

146. **Nectophryne kempi** Boulenger   (I)

The Garo Hills Tree Toad is a small toad with webbed toes, having truncated discs at the tips of fingers only. The tips of the toes are broadly rounded. The fingers are webbed about one-third of their length. The interorbital space is broader than the upper eyelid. The parotid gland is prominent and elliptical in shape. The tympanum is hidden.

Distribution : This toad is so far known from Tura in Garo Hills, Meghalaya.

Habits and habitat : Nothing in particular is known about the habits and habitat of this species, except that it is endemic to heavy rainfall area.

Status : Indeterminate. There is apparent rarity of this toad in most collections.

Bibliography

Ali, Salim. 1941. *The Book of Indian Birds.*

Ali, Salim. 1949. *Indian Hill Birds.*

Ali, Salim. and Ripley, S. D. 1969-1974. *Handbook of the Birds of India and Pakistan,* Vols. 1-10.

Baker, E. C. Stuart. 1908-1930. *The Game Birds of India, Burma and Ceylon,* Vols. 1-3.

Baker, E. C. Stuart. 1927-1930. *The Fauna of British India, Birds,* Vols. 1-8.

Beebe, W. 1918-1922. *A Monograph of the Pheasants,* Vols. I-IV.

Blanford, W. T. 1888-1891. *The Fauna of British India, Mammalia.*

Brander, A. A. Dunbar. 1923. *Wild Animals in Central India.*

Champion, F. W. 1927. *With a Camera in Tiger-Land.*

Champion, F. W. 1934. *The Jungle in Sunlight and Shadow.*

Corbett, J. M. 1944. *Man-Eaters of Kumaon.*

Elliot, D. G. 1882. *A Monograph of the Bucerotidae.*

Elliot, D. G. 1883. *A Monograph of the Felidae.*

Gee, E. P. 1964. *The Wild Life of India.*

Harper, F. 1945. *Extinct and Vanishing Mammals of the Old World.*

Hume, A. O. and Marshall, C. H. T. 1879-1881. *The Game Birds of India, Burmah and Ceylon,* Vols. 1-3.

Koffler, Ylla. 1958. *Animals in India.*

Lydekker, R. 1898. *The Deer of All Lands.*

Lydekker, R. 1898. *Wild Oxen, Sheep and Goats of All Lands.*

Lydekker, R. 1900. *The Great and Small Game of India, Burma and Tibet.*

Mukherjee, A. K. 1982. *Endangered Animals of India.*

Pocock, R. I. 1939-1941. *Fauna of British India, Mammalia* (2nd ed.) Vol. I-II.

Prater, S. H. 1948. *The Book of Indian Animals.*

Roonwal, M. L. and Mohnot, S. M. 1977. *Primates of South Asia.*

Saharia, V. B. (ed.) 1981. *Wild Life in India.*

Seshadri, B. 1969. *The Twilight of India's Wild Life.*

Shahi, S. P. 1977. *Back to the Wall : Saga of Wildlife in Bihar-India.*

Sankhla, K. S. 1978. *Tiger.*

Sclater, P. L. and Thomas, O. 1894-1900. *Book of Antelopes,* Vols. I-IV.

Stracey, P. D. 1963. *Wildlife in India.*

APPENDIX I
Indian Board for Wild Life (IBWL)

In 1950, an ad hoc committee was formed under the Chairmanship of the Inspector General of Forests, to suggest ways and means to safeguard the wildlife of India. This Committee recommended the constitution of a Central Board for Wild Life. The latter was constituted in 1952, as an advisory body to the Government of India. It initially consisted of 23 members, with Dr. S. L. Hora, the then Director Zoological Survey of India as its first Honorary Secretary. At its first meeting held at Mysore late in the same year, the Board constituted an Executive Committee for carrying out the day to day functions and to take decisions on its behalf. This Board was later redesignated as the Indian Board for Wild Life (IBWL) to indicate its national character, and the number of its members was increased to around seventy.

The Indian Board for Wild Life consists of Government officials as well as non-government members who are naturalists of eminence. It has a Chairman, two Vice-chairmen, a member Secretary, four Regional representatives (one each for north, south, east and west), and the Director, Zoological Survey of India, the Director, Botanical Survey of India, and the Chief Conservator of Forests, of different states, as members. In addition, Natural History Societies, Wildlife Preservation Societies and Bird Watcher's Societies are also represented on the Board. The IBWL also has a Bird Wing, a Zoo Wing and a Flora Wing for detailed consideration of matters with which they are concerned and for making appropriate recommendations to IBWL. The Prime Minister herself now adorns the chair-personship of the Indian Board for Wild Life. Members other than those who are members of office or appointment held by them, hold office for a period of four years. A member of Parliament, nominated as a member of the Board, continues for four years, unless he ceases to be a member. The Board is reconstituted after every four years unless otherwise ordered.

The Board is the main advisory body to the Government of India on the subject of wildlife conservation. It is supposed to meet once in a year and its standing committee, once in three months. The meetings of the Board may be held in rotation in each of the four regions of the country as well as at the Centre. In the States, State Wildlife Advisory Boards have also been constituted, on whom rests the main task of implementing the recommendations and decisions of the central body.

The Indian Board for Wild Life has the following main functions :

(i) to devise ways and means for the conservation and control of wildlife through coordinated legislative and practical measures with particular reference to seasonal and regional closures and the declaration of certain species of animals as protected animals and for the prevention of indiscriminate killing.

(ii) to sponsor the setting up of national parks, wildlife sanctuaries and zoological gardens and parks.

(iii) to promote public interest in wildlife and its preservation in harmony with the natural and human environment.

(iv) to advise the government on policy in respect of export of living animals, trophies, skins, furs, feathers and other wildlife products.

(v) to prevent cruelty to birds and beasts caught alive.

(vi) to review from time to time the progress in the field of wildlife conservation in the country and to suggest such measures for improvement as are considered necessary.

(vii) to perform such other functions as are germane to the purposes for which the Board has been constituted.

(viii) to assist and encourage the formation of wildlife societies and to act as a Central Coordinating Agency for all such bodies.

(ix) to advise the Central Government on any matter that it may refer to the Board, provided the subject matter of the reference falls within the prescribed functions of the Board.

(x) to do all such other things either alone or in conjugation with others or on the direction of the Government of India, which the Board may consider necessary, advisable or conducive to the preservation and conservation of wildlife or for other similar purposes for which it is constituted, including those mentioned herein.

The Board shall appoint a Standing Committee to :

(i) watch the implementation of the recommendations of the Board and to aid and advise the Central and State Governments on any matter arising therefrom;

(ii) carry out all such functions of the Board as the Board may, from time to time, delegate to it, as well as to take action on behalf of the Board while it is not in session; and

(iii) constitute specialised committees, sub-committees and study-groups as may be necessary from time to time, for the proper discharge of the functions of the Board.

The Board may also constitute committees or study groups for considering specialised subjects or matters.

The IBWL has discharged its responsibilities very efficiently. Some of the main achievements of the IBWL over the years are mentioned below :—

(i)   The most important achievement is the promulgation of the Indian Wild life (Protection) Act in 1972 for providing special legal protection to our wildlife and to the endangered species of fauna in particular, which have been appropriately listed in different Schedules. The Schedules are suitably amended from time to time. This Act has been adopted by all the States and Union Territories of the country except Jammu and Kashmir which has its own legislation on the pattern of the central one.

(ii)   A Zoological Park was set up in Delhi in 1955 reflecting the latest ideas of exhibiting animals in open air enclosures. The number of wildlife reserves has been increased from 33 to 256, of which 45 are National Parks and 211 Sanctuaries.

Forests and protection of wild animals and birds have been included in the concurrent list in the Constitution by the 42nd Amendment, in 1976. By virtue of this provision, not only can Central Government control their preservation and protection, but certain forests and sanctuaries can be acquired by the Government under its power of acquisition of property.

(iii)   On the recommendation of the IBWL, India became a party to the CITES in 1976, due to which the illegal trade in wildlife and its products has declined drastically.

(iv)   On the initiation of the IBWL, a National Environmental Conservation Policy and a National Forest Policy have been drafted. In the latter, emphasis has been given on the conservation rather than the exploitation of the forest resources.

The Government of India has reconstituted the Indian Board for Wild Life or 6th July 1983 as follows :—

1.	Chairperson	— Prime Minister of India
2.	Vice-Chairperson	— Union Minister for Agriculture
3.	Vice-Chairperson	— Union Deputy Minister for Environment.
4.	Member	— Union Minister of State for Defence
5-7.	Members	— Three Members representing the Parliament of India — two from Lok Sabha and one from Rajya Sabha.
8.	Member	— Chairman, Animal Welfare Board
9.	Member	— Secretary, Department of Environment
10.	Member	— Secretary, Department of Agriculture & Cooperation
11.	Member	— Secretary, Ministry of Commerce
12.	Member	— Secretary, Department of Education

13.	Member	— Secretary, Ministry of Information and Broadcasting
14.	Member	— Inspector General of Forests
15.	Member	— Financial Advisor, Department of Environment
16.	Member	— Director, Botanical Survey of India
17.	Member	— Director, Zoological Survey of India
18.	Member	— Director, Wildlife Institute of India
19.	Member	— Director General of Tourism
20.	Member	— President, Forest Research Institute & College.
21.	Member	— Director, Project Tiger
22-31	Members	— One representative each from 10 States & Union Territories by rotation, as may be decided by Government of India from time to time. Such representative would be nominated by the concerned State Government/Union Territory Administration and would represent the wild life organisation in the State/Union Territory.
32.	Member	— President, Bombay Natural History Society.
33.	Member	— President, Board of Trustees, World Wildlife Fund-India.
34.	Member	— President, Wildlife Preservation Society, Dehra Dun.
35.	Member	— President, Nilgiri Wildlife Association.
36.	Member	— Chairman, Assam Valley Wildlife Preservation Society.
37.	Member	— Chairman, Kerala High Range Wildlife Society.
38-47.	Members	— Such other members as may be nominated by the Government of India from amongst eminent naturalists, conservationists and ecologists.
48.	Member Secretary	— Joint Secretary (Wild Life) and Director, Wildlife Preservation , Department of Environment, Government of India.

Appendix II

Indian Wild Life (Protection) Act and its Schedules

As mentioned earlier, a comprehensive central legislation was enacted in 1972, called "The Wild Life (Protection) Act, 1972" to provide protection to wild animals, birds, reptiles, amphibians, insects, etc., and for matters connected therewith or ancillary or incidental thereto. The unique feature of this Act is that for the first time a uniform law on the subject was brought forth, which is applicable to the entire country except Jammu and Kashmir.

The Act has seven chapters dealing with the definitions; hunting of wild animals; authorities to be appointed or constituted under the Act; formation of Wildlife Sanctuaries, National Parks, Nature Reserves and closed areas; regulation of trade or commerce in wild animals, animal products and trophies; prevention and detection of offences; and the last dealing with miscellaneous regulations, followed by Schedules I to V. These Schedules are being suitably amended from time to time.

Schedule I lists the rare and endangered species which are totally protected throughout the country, live or dead or part thereof; Schedule II lists special game species which deserve more stringent protection for which licences can be issued under special circumstances; Schedule III and IV comprise special and small games; and Schedule V deals with vermins.

A list of species of mammals, birds, reptiles and amphibians included in different Schedules of the Indian Wild Life (Protection) Act, 1972, as amended up to 1980, is given below.

Schedules of the Wild Life (Protection) Act, 1972,
consequent to their amendments up to October, 1980.

Schedule I

PART I : MAMMALS

1	Andaman Wild Pig *(Sus scrofa andamanensis)*
1A	Bharal *(Pseudois nayur)*
1B	Binturong *(Arctictis binturong)*
2	Blackbuck *(Antelope cervicapra)*
2A*	
3	Browantlered Deer or Thamin *(Cervus eldi)*
3A	Capped Langur *(Presbytis pileatus)*
4	Caracal *(Felis caracal)*
4A	Cetecean species

5	Cheetah *(Acinonyx jubatus)*
5A	Chinese Pangolin *(Manis pentadactyla)*
5B	Chinkara or Indian Gazelle *(Gazella gazella bennetti)*
6	Clouded leopard *(Neofelis nebulosa)*
6A	Crabeating Macaque *(Macaca irus umbrosa)*
6B	Desert Cat *(Felis silvestris ornata)*
7	Dugong *(Dugong dugon)*
8	Fishing Cat *(Felis viverrina)*
8A	Fourhorned Antelope *(Tetracerus quadricornis)*
8B*	
8C	Flying Squirrels (all species of the genera *Hylopetes, Petaurista, Belomys & Eupetaurus)*
9	Golden Cat *(Felis temmincki)*
10	Golden Langur *(Presbytis geei)*
10A	Himalayan Ibex *(Capra ibex)*
10B	Himalayan Tahr *(Hemitragus jemlahicus)*
11	Hispid Hare *(Caprolagus hispidus)*
11A	Hog-Badger *(Arctonyx collaris)*
12	Hoolock *(Hylobates hoolock)*
12A*	
12B	Indian Elephant *(Elephas maximus)*
13	Indian Lion *(Panthera leo persica)*
14	Indian Wild Ass *(Equus hemionus khur)*
15	Indian Wolf *(Canis lupus pallipes)*
16	Kashmir Stag *(Cervus elaphus hanglu)*
16A	Leaf Monkey *(Presbytis phayrei)*
16B	Leopard or Panther *(Panthera pardus)*
17	Leopard Cat *(Felis bengalensis)*
18	Lesser or Red Panda *(Ailurus fulgens)*
19	Liontailed Macaque *(Macaca silenus)*
20	Slender Loris *(Loris tardigradus)*
21	Lynx *(Felis lynx isabellinus)*
22	Malabar Civet *(Viverra megaspila)*
22A	Malayan Sun Bear *(Helarctos malayanus)*
23	Marbled Cat *(Felis marmorata)*
24	Markhor *(Capra falconeri)*
24A	Mouse-Deer *(Tragulus meminna)*
25	Musk Deer *(Moschus moschiferus)*
25A	Nilgiri Tahr *(Hemitragus hylocrius)*
26	Nayan *(Ovis ammon hodgsoni)*
27	Pallas's Cat *(Felis manul)*
28	Pangolin *(Manis crassicaudata)*
29	Pygmy Hog *(Sus salvanius)*
29A	Retel *(Mellivora capensis)*
30	Rhinoceros *(Rhinoceros unicornis)*
31	Rustyspotted Cat *(Felis rubiginosa)*

31A	Serow *(Capricornis sumatraensis)*
31B	Sloth Bear *(Melursus ursinus)*
32	Slow Loris *(Nycticebus coucang)*
32A	Small Travancore Flying Squirrel *(Petinomys fuscocapillus)*
33	Snow Leopard *(Panthera uncia)*
34	Spotted Linsang *(Prionodon pardicolor)*
35	Swamp Deer (All subspecies of *Cervus duvauceli)*
36	Takin or Mishmi.Takin *(Budorcas taxicolor)*
36A	Tibetan Antelope or Chiru *(Pantholops hodgsoni)*
37	Tibetan Gazelle *(Procapra picticaudata)*
38	Tibetan Wild Ass *(Asinus kiang)*
39	Tiger *(Panthera tigris)*
40	Urial or Shapu *(Ovis vignei)*
41	Wild Buffalo *(Bubalus bubalis)*
41A	Wild Yak *(Bos grunniens)*

PART II : AMPHIBIANS AND REPTILES

1	Agra Monitor Lizard *(Varanus griseus)*
1B	Barred, Oval or Yellow Monitor Lizard *(Varanus flavescens)*
1C	Crocodiles (both the Estuarine and Marsh Crocodiles, *Crocodylus porosus* and *Crocodylus palustris)*
2	Gharial *(Gavialis gangeticus)*
3	Ganges Softshelled Turtle *(Trionyx gangeticus)*
4	Green Sea Turtle *(Chelonia mydas)*
5	Hawksbill Turtle *(Eretmochelys imbricata)*
6	Himalayan Newt or Salamandar *(Tylototriton verrucosus)*
7	Indian Eggeating Snake *(Elachistodon westermanni)*
8	Indian Flapshelled Turtle *(Lissemys punctata punctata)*
9	Indian Tent Turtle *(Kachuga tecta tecta)*
10	Large Bengal Monitor Lizard *(Varanus bengalensis)*
11	Leathery Turtle *(Dermochelys coriacea)*
12	Logger Head Turtle *(Caretta caretta)*
13	Olive-pack Logger Head Turtle *(Lepidochelys olivacea)*
14	Peacockmarked or Softshelled Turtle *(Trionyx hurum)*
14A	Pythons *(Python sp.)*
17A	Water Lizard *(Varanus salvator)*

PART III : BIRDS

1	Andaman Teal *(Anas gibberifrons albogularis)*
1A	Assam Bamboo Partridge *(Bambusicola fytchii)*
1B	Bazas *(Aviceda jerdoni* and *Aviceda leuphotes)*
1C	Bengal Florican *(Eupodotis bengalensis)*
1D	Black-necked Crane *(Grus nigricollis)*
1E	Blood Pheasants *(Ithaginis cruentus tibetanus, Ithaginis cruentus kuseri)*

2	Cheer pheasant *(Catreus wallichii)*
2A	Eastern White Stork *(Ciconia ciconia boyciana)*
2B	Forest Spotted Owlet *(Athene blewitti)*
3	Great Indian Bustard *(Ardeotis nigriceps)*
4	Great Pied Hornbill *(Buceros bicornis)*
4A	Hawks *(Accipitridae)*
4B	Hooded Crane *(Grus monacha)*
4C	Hornbills *(Ptilolaemus tickelli austeni, Aceros nipalensis, Rhyticeros undulatus ticehursti)*
4D	Houbara Bustard *(Chlamydotis undulata)*
4E	Hume's Bartailed Pheasant *(Syrmaticus humiae)*
4F	Indian Pied Hornbill *(Anthracoceros malabaricus)*
5	Jerdon's Courser *(Cursorius bitorquatus)*
6	Lammergeier *(Gypaetus barbatus)*
7	Large Falcons *(Falco peregrinus, Falco biarmicus* and *Falco chicquera)*
7A	Large Whistling Teal *(Anatidae)*
7B	Monal Pheasants *(Lophophorus impejanus, L. sclateri)*
8	Mountain Quail *(Ophrysia superciliosa)*
9	Narcondam Hornbill *(Rhyticeros (undulatus) narcondami)*
10	Nicobar Megapode *(Megapodius freycinet)*
10A	Nicobar Pigeon *(Caloenas nicobarica)*
10B	Osprey or Fisheating Eagle *(Pandion haliaetus)*
10C	Peacock Pheasant *(Polyplectron bicalcaratum)*
11	Peafowl *(Pavo cristatus)*
12	Pinkheaded Duck *(Rhodonessa caryophyllacea)*
13	Sclater's Monal *(Lophophorus sclateri)*
14	Siberian White Crane *(Grus leucogeranus)*
14A	
14B	Tibetan Snow cock *(Tetraogallus tibetanus)*
15	Tragopan pheasants *(Tragopan melanocephalus, Tragopan blythii, Tragopan satyra, Tragopan temminckii)*
16	Whitebellied Sea Eagle *(Haliaeetus leucogaster)*
17	White Eared Pheasant *(Crossoptilon crossoptilon)*
17A	White Spoonbill *(Platalea leucorodia)*
18	White-winged Wood Duck *(Cairina scutulata)*

SCHEDULE   II

SPECIAL GAME

PART   I

1	X
1A	Assamese Macaque *(Macaca assamensis)*
2	Bengal Porcupine *(Atherurus macrourus assamensis)*

3	Bison or Gaur *(Bos gaurus)*
3A	Bonnet Macaque *(Macaca radiata)*
3	XXX
4	X
4A	Common Langur *(Presbytis entellus)*
5	X
6	X
7	Ferret-Badgers *(Melogale moschata* and *Melogale personata)*
8	X
9	XXX
10	XXX
11	Himalayan Crestless Porcupine *(Hystrix hodgsoni)*
12	X
13	X
14	X
15	X
16	Pigtailed Macaque *(Macaca nemestrina)*
17	X
17A	Rhesus Macaque *(Macaca mulatta)*
18	X
19	Stumptailed Macaque (Macaca arctoides)
20	X
21	X
22	Wild Dog or Dhole *(Cuon alpinus)*
23	X
24	Chameleon *(Chamaeleon zeylanicus)*
25	Spinytailed lizard or Sanda *(Uromastix hardwickii)*

PART II

1A	Giant Squirrels *(Ratufa macroura, R. indica* and *R. bicolor)*
2	Himalayan Brown Bear *(Ursus arctos)*
2A	Himalayan Black Bear *(Selenarctos thibetanus)*
3	Nilgiri Langur *(Presbytis johni)*
4	Otters *(Lutra lutra, L. perspicillata, Aonyx cinerea)*
5	Sloth Bear *(Melursus ursinus)*
6	Tibetan Wolf *(Canis lupus chanco)*

SCHEDULE III

(SEE SECTIONS 2, 8, 9, 10, 11 and 61)

BIG GAME

1	X
2	Barking Deer or Muntjac *(Muntiacus muntjak)*
3	X
4	X
5	Chital *(Axis axis)*
6	X
7	Gorals *(Nemorhaedus goral, Nemorhaedus hodgsoni)*
8	XX
9	X
10	X
11	Hog Deer *(Axis porcinus)*
12	Hyena *(Hyaena hyaena)*
13	X
14	Nilgai *(Boselaphus tragocamelus)*
15	X
16	Sambar *(Cervus unicolor)*
17	X
18	XX
19	Wild Pig *(Sus scrofa)*

SCHEDULE IV

SMALL GAME

1	Civets (all species of Viverridae except Malabar Civet)
1A	Common Fox
2	Desert Fox *(Vulpes vulpes)*
3	Ermine *(Mustela erminea)*
3A	Fivestriped Palm Squirrel *(Funambulus pennanti)*
4	Hares *(Lepus nigricollis* and *Ochotona sp.)*
4A	Hedgehog *(Hemiechinus auritus)*
4B	Jungle Cat *(Felis chaus)*
4C	Little Indian Porpoise *(Neomeris phocaenoides)*
4D	Jackal *(Canis aureus)*
4E	Indian Porcupine *(Hystrix indica)*
5	Marmots *(Marmota bobak himalayana, Marmota caudata)*
6	Martens *(Martes foina intermedia, Martes flavigula, Martes gwatkinsii)*
7	XXX
7A	Polecats *(Vormela peregusna, Mustela putorius)*
8	Red Fox *(Vulpes vulpes)*
8A	Red Fox *(Vulpes montana, V. griffithi, V. pusilla)*
9	Tibetan Fox *(Vulpes ferrilata)*

9A X
10 Weasels *(Mustela sibirica, Mustela kathia* and *Mustela altaica)*

11 Birds :

1.   Avadavat (Estrildinae)
2.   Avocet (Recurvirostridae)
3.   Babblers (Timaliinae)
4.   Barbets (Capitonidae)
5.   Barn Owls (Tytoninae)
6.   Bitterns (Ardeidae)
7.   Brown-headed Gull *(Larus brunnicephalus)*
8.   Bulbuls (Pycnonotidae)
9.   Buntings(Emberizidae)

10.   Bustards (Otididae)
11.   Bustard-Quails (Turnicidae)
12.   Chloropsis (Irenidae)
13.   Comb Duck *(Sarkidiornis melanotos)*
14.   Coot (Rallidae)
15.   Cormorants (Phalacrocoracidae)
16.   Cranes (Gruidae)
17.   Cuckoos (Cuculidae)
18.   Darters (Phalacrocoracidae)
19.   Doves including the Emerald Dove (Columbidae)
20.   Drongos (Dicruridae)
21.   Ducks (Anatidae)
22.   Egrets (Ardeidae)
23.   Fairy Blue Bird (Irenidae)
24.   Falcons (Falconidae) excepting the Shahin and Peregrine Falcons *(Falco peregrinus),* the Saker or Cherrug, Shanghar and Laggar Falcons, *(Falco biarmicus)* and the Redheaded Merlin *(F. chiquera).*
25.   Finches including the Chaffinch (Fringillidae)
26.   Flamingos (Phoenicopteridae)
27.   Flowerpeckers (Dicaeidae)
28.   Flycatchers (Muscicapidae)
29.   Geese (Anatidae)
30.   Goldfinch and allies (Carduelinae)
31.   Grebes (Podicipedidae)
32.   Herons (Ardeidae)
33.   Ibises (Thereskiornithidae)
34.   Ioras (Irenidae)
35.   Jays (Corvidae)
36.   Jacanas (Jacanidae)
37.   Kingfishers (Alcedinidae)
38.   Larks (Alaudidae)
39.   Lorikeets (Psittacidae)

40. Magpies including the Hunting Magpie (Corvidae)
41. Mannikins (Estrildinae)
42. Megapodes (Megapodidae)
43. Minivets (Campephagidae)
44. Munias (Estrildinae)
45 Mynas (Sturnidae)
46. Nightjars (Caprimulgidae)
47. Orioles (Oriolidae)
49. Oystercatchers (Haematopodidae)
50. Parakeets (Psittacidae)
51. Partridges (Phasianidae)
52. Pelicans (Pelecanidae)
53. Pheasants (Phasianidae)
54. Pigeons (Columbidae) excepting the Blue Rock Pigeon
   (Columba livia)
55. Pipits (Motacillidae)
56. Plovers (Charadriinae)
57. Quails (Phasianidae)
58. Rails (Rallidae)
59. Rollers or Blue Jay (Coraciidae)
60. Sandgrouses (Pteroclididae)
61. Sandpipers (Scolopacinae)
62. Snipes (Scolopacinae)
63. Spurfowls (Phasianidae)
64. Starlings (Sturnidae)
65. Stone Curlew (Burhinidae)
66. Storks (Ciconiidae)
67. Stilt (Recurvirostridae)
69. Swans (Anatidae)
70. Teals (Anatidae)
71. Thrushes (Turdinae)
72. Tits (Paridae)
73. Tree Pies (Corvidae)
74. Trogons (Trogonidae)
75. Vultures (Accipitridae)
76. Waxbills (Estrildinae)
77. Weaver Birds or Bayas (Ploceidae)
78. White-eyes (Zosteropidae)
79. Woodpeckers (Picidae)
80. Wrens (Troglodytidae)
48. Owls (Strigidae)
68. Sunbirds (Nectarnidae)

12. Snakes :
   i) Amblycephalidae
   ii) Anilidae
   iii) Boidae

  iv) Colubridae
  v) Desypeptidae (Egg-eating snakes)
  vi) Elaphidae (Cobras, Kraits and Coral snakes)
  vii) Glauconnidae
  viii) Hydrophiidae (Sea snakes)
  ix) Tylsiidae
  x) Leptotyphlopidae
  xi) Typhlopidae
  xii) Uropeltidae
  xiii) Viperidae
  xiv) Xenopeltidae

13. Fresh water Frog *(Rana sp.)*
14. Three keeled Turtle *(Melanochelys tricarinata)*
15. Tortoise (Testudinidae, Trionychidae)
16. Viviparous toads *(Nectophrynoides sp.)*
17. Voles

SCHEDULE V

1. Common Crow
2. XXX
3. Fruit Bats
4. XXX
5. Mice
6. Rats
7. XXXX

---

* This entry now comes under entry No. 4A Cetacean
sp. Schedule I Part I.

'X' denotes transferred to Schedule I
'XX' denotes transferred to Schedule II (Part I)
'XXX' denotes transferred to Schedule II (Part II)
'XXXX' denotes transferred to Schedule IV.

APPENDIX III

IUCN/WWF/WWF -INDIA/FAO and UNDP

The International Union for Conservation of Nature and Natural Resources (IUCN), founded in 1948, is the leading international, non-government organisation concerned with conservation. It is a network of both government and non-governmental organisations as well as scientists and conservation experts dedicated to the protection and sustainable use of living resources.

IUCN has more than 475 member-organisations, and 116 governmental agencies in 110 countries, which include the governments of 54 nations and virtually all major national and international non-governmental conservation organisations.

IUCN's six Commissions consist of some 1500 experts in ecology, environmental education, environmental planning, environmental policy, law and administration, national parks and protected areas, and the survival of species.

The IUCN secretariat conducts or facilitates IUCN's major functions : monitoring the status of conservation, developing plans for dealing with conservation problems (such as the World Conservation Strategy), promoting action on their plans by governments or organisations as appropriate, and providing advice and assistance to implement conservation. The Secretariat, further, coordinates communication between the members and the Commissions as well as the development, selection and management of WWF's (World Wildlife Fund) Conservation Projects around the World. IUCN also manages the United Nations Environment Programme (UNEP) and the CITES Secretariat which regulates the worldwide trade in endangered species of animals and plants. It also performs the continuing bureau duties under the Conservation of Wetlands of International Importance, especially of water-fowl habitats.

IUCN receives financial support from its own members, from WWF, UNEP and a number of other sources.

The World Wildlife Fund-International was set up in 1961. It is the world's largest voluntary organisation, raising funds for urgent conservation requirements and promoting conservation through a world wide education campaign and arousing public consciousness. Since October, 1979, it has its headquarters at Gland, Switzerland. HRH Prince Philip, the Duke of Edinburgh is the President of this body. The Giant Panda is the official symbol of WWF.

An Executive Committee, currently comprising the President and ten members of the Board of Trustees of WWF, is responsible to the Board for

270

the administration of the Fund. It supervises the raising and disbursement of funds as well as international education and information activities. It also prepares recommendations for the Board on matters of WWF policy.

WWF's Board of Trustees includes influential individuals from a wide variety of professions, such as science, finance, medicine, art, advertising, trade and diplomacy. These persons spare their time, energy and individual talents to help WWF to achieve its goal.

WWF depends entirely upon voluntary contributions for raising its fund. It is collected by National Organisations on five continents and through International Headquarters in Switzerland.

WWF raises money through (i) interest on an endowment fund of more than 10 million dollars contributed by 1001 persons from all parts of the World (ii) donations from the general public,(iii) contributions from its over one million regular members,(iv) grants from several charitable foundations, etc.

WWF works in close collaboration with IUCN and is supported by the United Nations Organisations (UNO), UNESCO, UNEP and FAO. It takes up conservation projects all over the World and has set up National Appeals everywhere. Up to 1981, WWF has provided 55 million dollars in financial support to some 2800 conservation projects in 130 countries. It has, further, supported 260 parks and reserves in five continents.

Conservation objectives are reviewed twice a year by the Conservation Programme Committee, composed of members from leading WWF National Organisations, Trustees and senior staff of WWF and IUCN.

WWF is a worldwide movement and relies on grass roots support. It has established affiliate organisations in major donor countries to support the ambitious fund-raising and educational objectives it has set.

While all WWF affiliate organisations share the use of the WWF name and panda symbol, they represent a broad spectrum of activities. They support conservation projects in their own territories as well as internationally. Each affiliate is entitled to allocate one-third of its income to domestic programmes. The remaining two-thirds are allocated to international projects through or in cooperation with WWF, using the scientific and technical advice of the IUCN. Till May, 1981, WWF had 26 affiliate organisations located in Australia, Austria, Belgium, Canada, Denmark, Finland, France, Hong Kong, India, Italy, Japan, Kenya, Luxembourg, Malaysia, Netherlands, New Zealand, Norway, Pakistan, South Africa, Spain, Sweden, Switzerland, Turkey, U.K., and U.S.A. In 1979, the Joint WWF-China Committee was formed to coordinate links between WWF and Chinese authorities and to initiate high priority conservation projects in China.

The World Wildlife Fund-India was formed in 1969. It has a Board of eight Trustees with its Headquarters in Bombay and three Regional Offices in Calcutta, Delhi and Madras. Its functions are as under :

It focuses the attention of the Government of India and of the State Governments on the problems of concern in the field of wildlife conservation.

It organises Conservation Education Programme both in educational institutions and for general public. As a part of youth movement, more than 400 'Nature Clubs' have been set up in four different regions (north, south, east and west) of India. It also publishes a quarterly bulletin and sells wildlife posters, calendars, greeting cards, etc., with messages on conservation printed over them.

It supports research projects on wildlife conservation in India, the foremost being the Project Tiger (1973), the Gir Ecological Research Project (1968), Project Hangul (1970), the Himalayan Musk Deer Project (1979) and the Lesser Cats Project. The last one has been taken up recently (1981) in collaboration with the Zoological Survey of India. WWF-India has not only funded these projects, but has also provided them vehicles, speed-boats, telecommunication equipments and many kinds of gadgets for the study of wildlife.

Under the Food and Agriculture Organization (FAO) of the UNO and United Nations Development Programme (UNDP), a major project for the conservation, management and breeding of crocodiles was started in India in 1975, with emphasis on the Gharial, the Mugger and the Estuarine Crocodile. As a result twelve sanctuaries in five states, covering an area of 21000 sq. km have come up, and several crocodile-breeding centres have been set up. The details are already given in the introductory portion.

APPENDIX   IV

INTERNATIONAL COUNCIL FOR BIRD PRESERVATION (ICBP)

International Council for Bird Preservation (ICBP) is the world's oldest international conservation organisation. It was founded in 1922. It is a federation of national (and some international) organisations, concerned with the conservation, management and wise utilisation of wild birds and their habitats. It is a charitable, non-profitmaking organisation, divided into National Sections. Although, some National Sections have government departments as members, ICBP is a non-government organisation.

In terms of its operational structure, ICBP can be described as a federation of units forming the different levels of a pyramid, each building upon the other for its effectiveness. In broad terms, the basic unit is the National Sections, composed of local societies (Member Organisations), which promote bird conservation in their home countries. However, the National Sections combine in various ways to facilitate the international action (Continental Sections, Council), since bird conservation issues often transcend national boundaries. The higher levels of the federation serve both to co-ordinate the activities of the National Sections and to further the overall aims of bird conservation on their behalf, which includes increasing the ICBP network by establishing new National Sections. The tip of the pyramid is the ICBP's annually reviewed programme of conservation activities and projects.

All National Sections are members of the Council, which meet once in four years (ICBP World Conference). They are entitled to vote in the election of officers and in the adoption of resolutions determining the Council's policies. The Council officers are led by a President together with a Chairman of the Executive Committee and a Treasurer. The Executive Committee is bound to act in accordance with the resolutions of the Council, but, in carrying out these resolutions, is free to appoint individuals, subcommittees, specialist groups and task forces and to direct the Secretariat as may be appropriate. The founder of this organisation is Dr. Jean Delacour. Dr. S. D. Ripley, the world renowned ornithologist was the President of the Council from 1958 to 1982. Dr. Russell W. Patterson has taken over as the new President in 1982.

The production of the so called 'Red Data Book' was initiated by ICBP for birds, with compiling of card files in the 1950's by the President, Prof. S. Dillon Ripley, assisted by ICBP members of the London, Paris and New York Museums of Natural History. ICBP also provides grants for useful and important bird conservation projects that are in accordance with the ICBP programme priorities.

The Expert Committee on Birds of the Indian Board for Wildlife is the National Section of the ICBP, which looks after all the matters pertaining to the preservation of Indian birds. The Convener of the Committee is Dr. B. K. Tikader, Director, Zoological Survey of India, Calcutta, and its Chairman is Dr. Salim Ali. Shri Samar Singh, Shri J. C. Daniel, Prof. Madhav Gadgil and one representative of the Government of Rajasthan directly concerned with the management of the Keoladeo National Park, are its members. Some of the major programmes of this organisation are the formulation of the policy on the control of export and import of birds and their products, and divising methods and proposing suitable suggestions to the Government of India for the conservation of rare and endangered birds. Recently, it has finalised a treaty concerning birds that migrate between India and USSR, for their better protection.

As mentioned above, the ICBP meets once in four years. Of the recent meetings, the fourteenth was held in 1966, in England, the fifteenth in 1970, in Netherlands, the sixteenth in 1974, in Australia, the seventeenth in 1978, in Yugoslavia, and the last in 1982, at Cambridge (U.K.).

APPENDIX — V

CONVENTION ON INTERNATIONAL TRADE IN ENDANGERED SPECIES OF WILD FAUNA AND FLORA (CITES)

In order to prevent over-exploitation of wild fauna and flora through international trade, a Convention on International Trade in Endangered Species of Wild Fauna and Flora (CITES) was signed at Washington on 3rd March, 1973, and after ratification by ten countries, namely, United States of America, Nigeria, Switzerland, Tunisia, Sweden, Cyprus, UAE, Ecuador, Chile and Uruguay, came into effect on 1st July, 1975. The Government of India signed this Convention in July, 1974, and became a party to it from 18 October, 1976. Under this Convention the Inspector General of Forests and the Director of Wildlife Preservation are the Management Authorities in India, supported by three Scientific Authorities namely, the Director, Zoological Survey of India, the Director, Botanical Survey of India and the Director, Central Marine Fisheries Research Institute. By May, 1983, 81 countries had signed this Convention.

The representatives of the parties meet every two years to review the Convention and its implementation. The first meeting of the CITES was held in Berne (Switzerland), in November, 1976, the second in Costa Rica in March 1979, the third in New Delhi (India) in February 1981 and the fourth in Gaberone, Botswana, in April 1983.

Aims and objectives :

The signatories to CITES agree —

(i) that wild fauna and flora in their many beautiful and varied forms are an irreplaceable part of the natural systems of the earth.

(ii) that they are conscious of the ever-growing value of wild fauna and flora from aesthetic, scientific, cultural, recreational and economic points of view.

(iii) that people and States are and should be the best protectors of their own wild fauna and flora.

274

(iv)   that international cooperation is essential for the protection of certain species of wild fauna and flora against over-exploitation through international trade.

(v)   that there is an urgency of taking appropriate measures to this end.

Keeping the above-mentioned objectives in view, the contracting nations of the Convention framed rules and regulations to control the worldwide trade in endangered wildlife and its products. The Convention itself is deposited with the Swiss Government and has texts in five languages : Chinese, English, French, Russian and Spanish. It consists of 25 articles, outlines of which are given below.

Article 1 defines the terms used in the Convention. In particular, it states that the Convention covers animals or plants alive or dead, plus any readily recognisable part or derivative thereof.

Article II outlines the fundamental principles. Endangered species are listed in three appendices :

Appendix I lists species threatened with extinction.

Appendix II lists species not yet threatened but which could become endangered if trade is not controlled. Those species are also included here, if it is difficult to distinguish them from other species mentioned in Appendix I and II. This is to make it difficult for illegal trade to take place through misidentification.

Article III regulates trade in species included in Appendix I. An export permit from the country of origin and an import permit from the country of importation are required. These permits are issued by the National Management Authorities stating that their removal from the country of origin will not be detrimental to the survival of the species and that the motive is not primarily commercial. Live specimens must be properly shipped and housed.

Article IV regulates trade in species included in Appendix II. An export permit from the country of origin is required, but not an import permit. Conditions are similar to Appendix I species but there is no restriction on the specimen being used for commercial purposes.

Article V regulates trade in Appendix III species. The import requires a certificate of origin. If the import is from the State that has included the species on Appendix III, an export permit is required.

Article VI concerns the format of permits and certificates. A separate permit is required for each consignment; an export permit is only valid for six months.

Article VII relates to exemptions relating to trade. Exemptions include :

- A specimen acquired before the convention came into force.

- The reimport of specimens that are personal or household effects.

- Appendix I species bred in captivity for commercial purpose or plants artificially propagated are to be treated as specimens of species of· Appendix II.

- The noncommercial loan and exchange of specimens between scientists and museums, etc.

- Specimens which form part of the travelling zoos,circuses or exhibitions.

Article VIII describes enforcement, which is the exclusive responsibility of the member States. Penalties may include fines, imprisonment, the confiscation of specimens or their return to the State of export. Rescue centres must be provided for confiscated live specimens.

Article IX describes the Management Authority and Scientific Authority which each State must have. The former is responsible for issuing permits, subject to advice from the Scientific Authority. The latter is expected to notify the CITES Secretariat if it believes that trade in any species should be limited.

Article X states that where trade is with the non-CITES country, comparable documents to those required by the Convention may be accepted.

Article XI requires meeting of the Parties every two years, to review the working of the Convention and amend the Appendices. UN agencies and non-member States may attend and speak as observers. An extraordinary meeting may be called at any time if two-third Party-members agree.

Article XII concerns with the organisation and functions of the Secretariat provided by the Executive Director of the United Nations Environment Programme. He may be assisted by suitable inter-governmental or non-governmental international or national agencies and bodies technically qualified in protection, conservation and management of wild fauna and flora.

Article XIII provides for communication between Parties and the Secretariat when a species is being adversely affected by trade.

Article XIV states that CITES has no effect on domestic legislation or on other international conventions. States may enforce stricter domestic measures.

Article XV deals with amendments to Appendices I and II. Any Party may propose an amendment for consideration at a meeting of the Parties, provided the text has been circulated 150 days in advance and the comments of other States over it are circulated 30 days in advance. An amendment is adopted by two-third majority; it comes into force 90 days after the meeting. Amendments may also be made between meetings, by a postal vote in which half of the Parties must vote.

Article XVI describes procedure for amendments to Appendix III. Any party may submit a list of species for Appendix III. This list is sent as quickly as possible to other Parties, and takes effect 90 days later.

Article XVII provides for the amendment of the Convention through an extraordinary meeting of the Parties, convened by the Secretariat on the written request of at least one-third of the Parties. Such amendments shall be adopted by a two-third majority of Parties present and voting.

Article XVIII provides that any dispute arising between two Parties with respect to the interpretation or application of the provisions of the present Convention shall be subject to negotiation between the Parties involved in the dispute or the Parties may submit the dispute to arbitration at the Hague, and the Parties shall be bound by the arbitral decision.

Article XIX, XX, XXI, concern signature, ratification and accession. The Washington Convention was open for signature from 3 March, 1973 to 31 December, 1974. States which signed, may ratify the Convention at any time. Instruments of ratification, acceptance or approval shall be deposited with the Government of the Swiss Confederation which shall be the Depository Government.

Article XXII states that the Convention comes into force in a country 90 days after the country has ratified or acceded.

Article XXIII states that any Party may place a specific reservation on one or more species in any of the three Appendices I, II and III, and on parts and derivatives of Appendix II species.

Article XXIV refers to the denunciation of the Convention by any Party at any time. The denunciation shall take effect twelve months after the Depository Government has received the notification.

Article XXV describes the Depository Government.

A list of the species of mammals, birds, reptiles and amphibians from the Indian Union included in Appendices I and II of the CITES is given below, preceded by the interpretation thereon.

INTERPRETATION :

1. Species included in these Appendices are referred to :
    a) by the name of the species; or
    b) as being all of the species included in a higher taxon or designate part thereof.

2. The abbreviation "spp" is used to denote all species of a higher taxon.

3. Other references to taxa higher than species are for the purposes of information or classification only.

4. The abbreviation "p.e." is used to denote species which are possibly extinct.

5. An asterisk (*) placed against the name of a species or higher taxon indicates that one or more geographically separate populations, subspecies or species of that species or taxon are included in Appendix I and that these populations, subspecies or species are excluded from Appendix II.

6. Two asterisks (**) placed against the name of a species or higher taxon indicate that one or more geographically separate populations, subspecies or species of that species or taxon are included in Appendix II and that these populations, subspecies or species are excluded from Appendix I.

7. The symbol (+) followed by a number placed against the name of a species or higher taxon denotes that only designated geographically separate population, subspecies or species of that species or taxon are included in the Appendix concerned, as follows,

    + 201 Population of South America
    + 202 Population of Bhutan, India, Nepal and Pakistan
    + 203 Italian population
    + 204 All North American subspecies
    + 205 Asian population
    + 206 Indian population
    + 207 Australian population
    + 208 Himalayan population
    + 209 All New Zealand species
    + 210 Population of Chile
    + 211 All species of the family in America
    + 212 Australian population

278

8. The symbol (—) followed by a number placed against the name of a species or higher taxon denotes that designated geographically separate populations, subspecies, species, groups of species or families of that species or taxon are excluded from the Appendix concerned, as follows :

- 101 Population of Bhutan, India, Nepal and Pakistan
- 102 *Panthera tigris altaica* (= *amurensis*)
- 103 Australian population
- 104 Cathartidae
- 105 Population of North America, except Greenland
- 106 Population of the United States of America
- 107 *Melopsittacus undulatus, Nymphicus hollandicus,* and *Psittacula krameri*
- 108 Population of Papua New Guinea
- 109 Population of Chile

- 110 All species which are not succulent

APPENDIX I*

MAMMLIA (Mammals)

PRIMATES

Ceropithecidae	*Macaca silenus*	Lion-tailed Macaque
	Presbytis entellus	Entellus Monkey or Common Langur or Hanuman Langur
	Presbytis geei	Golden Langur
	Presbytis pileatus	Capped Langur
Hylobatidae	*Hylobates* spp.	Gibbons

LAGOMORPHA

Leporidae	*Caprolagus hispidus*	Hispid Hare

CETACEA

Platanistidae	*Platanista* spp.	Gangetic Dolphin or Susu
Physeteridae	*Physeter catodon* (= *macrocephalus)*	Sperm Whale
Phocaenidae	*Neomeris phocaenoides*	Black Finless Porpoise
Balaenopteridae	*Balaenoptera musculus*	Great Blue Whale
	Balaenoptera physalus	Common Rorqual or Finback
	Balaenoptera borealis	Sei Whale

---

* Appendix I and II here denote that of CITES.

CARNIVORA

Canidae	*Canis lupus* ** +202	Wolf
Ursidae	*Helarctos malayanus*	Malayan Sun Bear
	Selenarctos thibetanus	Asian Black Bear
	Ursus arctos isabellinus	Himalayan Brown Bear or Red Bear
Mustelidae	*Lutra lutra*	Common or Indian Otter
Viverridae	*Prionodon pardicolor*	Spotted Linsang or Tiger Civet
Felidae	*Acinonyx jubatus*	Cheetah
	Felis bengalensis bengalensis	Leopard Cat
	Felis caracal ** +205	Caracal
	Felis marmorata	Marbled Cat
	Felis rubiginosa ** +206	Rustyspotted Cat
	Felis temmincki	Golden Cat
	Neofelis nebulosa	Clouded Leopard
	Panthera leo persica	Asian Lion
	Panthera pardus	Leopard or Panther
	Panthera tigris ** — 102	Tiger
	Panthera uncia	Snow Leopard

PROBOSCIDEA

Elephantidae	*Elephas maximus*	Asian Elephant

SIRENIA

Dugongidae	*Dugong dugon* ** — 103	Sea Cow or Dugong

PERISSODACTYLA

Equidae	*Equus (= Asinus) hemionus khur*	Indian Wild Ass
Rhinocerotidae	*Rhinocerotidae* spp.	Rhinoceros

ARTIODACTYLA

Suidae	*Sus salvanius*	Pygmy Hog
Cervidae	*Cervus duvauceli*	Swamp Deer or Barasinga
	Cervus elephus hanglu	Hangul or Kashmir Stag
	Cervus eldi	Thamin or Brow-antlered Deer

	Moschus moschiferus ** +208	Musk Deer
Bovidae	*Bos gaurus*	Indian Bison or Gaur
	Bos mutus	Yak
	Capra falconeri jerdoni	Suleiman Markhor
	Capricornis sumatraensis	Serow
	Nemorhaedus goral	Goral
	Ovis ammon hodgsoni	Nayan or Great Tibetan Sheep
	Ovis vignei	Shapu or Urial
	Pantholops hodgsoni	Tibetan Antelope or Chiru

AVES (Birds)

PELECANIFORMES
Fregatidae — *Fregata andrewsi* — Christmas Island Frigate Bird

CICONIIFORMES
Ciconiidae — *Ciconia ciconia boyciana* — Eastern White Stork

ANSERIFORMES
Anatidae — *Cairina scutulata* — White Winged Wood Duck

Rhodonessa caryophyllacea p.e. — Pinkheaded Duck

FALCONIFORMES
Accipitridae — *Aquila heliaca* — Imperial Eagle
Falconidae — *Falco peregrinus (peregrinoides/ babylonicus)* — Red Capped or Barbary Falcon

GALLIFORMES

Phasianidae
	Catreus wallichii	Cheer Pheasant
	Crossoptilon crossoptilon	Eared Pheasant
	Lophophorus impejanus	Impeyan or Himalayan Monal Pheasant
	Lophophorus sclateri	Sclater's Monal Pheasant
	Syrmaticus humiae	Mrs. Humes Barbacked Pheasant
	Tetraogallus tibetanus	Tibetan Snowcock
	Tragopan blythii	Grey-bellied Tragopan
	Tragopan melanocephalus	Western Horned Tragopan

GRUIFORMES

Gruidae	*Grus leucogeranus*	Siberian or Great White Crane
	Grus monacha	Hooded Crane
	Grus nigricollis	Blacknecked Crane
Otididae	*Chlamydotis undulata*	Houbara Bustard
	Ardeotis nigriceps	Great Indian Bustard
	Eupodotis bengalensis	Bengal Florican

CULUMBIFORMES

Columbidae	*Caloenas nicobarica*	Nicobar Pigeon

STRIGIFORMES

Strigidae	*Athene blewitti*	Forest Spotted Owlet

CORACIFORMES

Bucerotidae	*Buceros bicornis homrai*	Great Pied Hornbill

REPTILIA (Reptiles)

TESTUDINATA

Emydidae	*Batagur baska*	Batagur
	Geoemyda (=Nicoria) tricarinata)	Three Keeled Turtle
	Kachuga tecta tecta	Indian Tent Turtle
Cheloniidae	*Cheloniidae* spp.	Marine Turtle
Dermochelyidae	*Dermochelys coriacea*	Leathery or Leatherback Turtle
Trionychidae	*Lissemys punctata punctata*	Indian Flapshelled Turtle
	Trionyx gangeticus	Gangetic Softshelled Turtle
	Trionyx hurum	Peacockmarked Turtle or Ocellated Softshelled Turtle

CROCODYLIA

Crocodylidae	*Crocodylus palustris*	Marsh Crocodile or Mugger
	Crocodylus porosus	Estuarine Crocodile
Gavialidae	*Gavialis gangeticus*	Gharial

RHYNCHOCEPHALIA

Varanidae	*Varanus bengalensis*	Common Indian Monitor
	Varanus flavescens	Yellow Monitor
	Varanus griseus	Indian Desert Monitor

SERPENTES

Boidae	*Python molurus molurus*	Indian Python

AMPHIBIA (Amphibians)

SALIENTIA

Bufonidae	*Nectophrynoides* spp.	Webbed-footed or Tree Toads

APPENDIX — II

MAMMALIA

PRIMATES	PRIMATES spp. *	Apes, monkeys & lemurs
PHOLIDOTA		
Manidae	*Manis crassicaudata*	Indian Pangolin or Scaly Anteater
	Manis pentadactyla	Chinese Pangolin
RODENTIA		
Sciuridae	*Ratufa* spp.	Giant Squirrels
CETACEA	*CETACEA* spp *	Whales, dolphins & porpoises
CARNIVORA		
Canidae	*Cuon alpinus*	Asian Wild Dog or Dhole
Procyonidae	*Ailurus fulgens*	Red Panda or Lesser Panda or Cat-Bear
Mustelidae	*Lutrinae* spp. *	Otters
Felidae	*Felidae* spp. *	Desert, Fishing, Jungle, & Pallas's Cat & Lynx
PERISSODACTYLA		
Equidae	*Equus hemionus* * (*=Asinus kiang)*	Tibetan Wild Ass
ARTIODACTYLA		
Bovidae	*Capra falconeri*	Markhor

AVES

PELECANIFORMES

Pelecanidae	*Pelecanus crispus*	Dalmatian Pelican

CICONIIFORMES

Ciconiidae	*Ciconia nigra*	Black Stork
Threskiornithidae	*Platalea leucorodia*	White Spoonbill

ANSERIFORMES

Anatidae	*Cygnus bewickii Jankowskii*	Jankowskis or Eastern Whistling Swan
	Sarkidiornis melanotos	Comb Duck or Nukta

FALCONIFORMES	*FALCONIFORMES* spp. * —104	Eagles, falcons, hawks, & vultures

GALLIFORMES

Megapodiidae	*Megapodius freycinet abbotti*	South Nicobar Megapode
	Megapodius freycinet nicobariensis	North Nicobar Megapode
Phasianidae	*Gallus sonneratii*	Grey Jungle Fowl
	Ithaginis cruentus	Blood Pheasant
	Polyplectron bicalcaratum	Peacock Pheasant

GRUIFORMES

Laridae	*Larus brunnicephalus*	Brown-headed Gull

PSITTACIFORMES	*PSITTACIFORMES* spp. * —107	Parrots
STRIGIFORMES	STRIGIFORMES spp. **	Owls & owlets

CORACIIFORMES

Bucerotidae	*Rhyticeros narcondami*	Narcondam Hornbill

PICIFORMES

Picidae	*Picus squamatus flavirostris*	Western Scalybellied Green Woodpecker

REPTILIA

TESTUDINATA

Testudinidae	*Testudinidae* spp. *	Tortoises
Pelomedusidae	*Pedocnemis* spp.	River Turtles or Side-neck Turtles

SERPENTES

Boidae	*Boidae* spp. *	Sand Boas
Colubridae	*Elachistodon westermanni*	Indian Egg-eating Snake

APPENDIX VI

Wildlife Sanctuaries and National Parks

Wildlife Sanctuary :

Place where some rare, wild, indigenous mammals, birds, reptiles and any other form of wildlife in good numbers and representative of a region are considered to be in need of protection together with the natural environment, the area is declared as a WILDLIFE SANCTUARY. It is created by the State Forest Department by Gazettee Notification. It can, therefore, be abolished in a similar manner.

National Park :

An area dedicated by statute (legislation) for all times to come, to conserve the natural or historical objects of national significance and to conserve wildlife therein, in such a manner, and by such means, as will leave them unimpared for the enjoyment of future generations, with such modifications as local conditions may demand. Since a National Park is created by Central Legislation, it has a permanent status.

LIST OF NATIONAL PARKS IN INDIA

Sl. No.	Name	Location/ District	Area (in Sq Km)	Important fauna
1	2	3	4	5
		ANDAMAN & NICOBAR		
1.*	Middle Butten	Andaman	0.44	—
2.*	North Butten	Andaman	0.44	—
3.*	South Butten	Andaman	0.04	—
4.*	Saddle Peak	Andaman	32.54	—
		ASSAM		
1.	Kaziranga	Sibsagar & Nowgong	430.00	Hoolock gibbon, Indian fox, sloth bear, tiger, leopard, sambar, hog deer, onehorned rhinoceros, elephant, gaur, wild buffalo, pangolin, grey pelican, partridge, florican, python.
		GUJARAT		
1.	Gir	Junagadh	140.40	Hyena, jungle cat, Asiatic lion, leopard, sambar, chital, chinkara, fourhorned antelope, mugger.
2.	Marine	Jamnagar	110.00	Common dolphin, sea turtle, fishes, molluscs, crustaceans.
3.	Valavadar	Bhavnagar	17.83	Wolf, blackbuck, fourhorned antelope, great Indian bustard.
4.	Vansda	Valsad	24.50	Leopard, sambar, chital.

1	2	3	4	5
		JAMMU & KASHMIR		
1.	Dachigam	Srinagar	141.00	Brown bear, black bear, leopard, hangul, musk deer, serow, pheasants.
2.	Hemis High Altitude National Park	Srinagar	300.00	— —
3.	Kistwar	Srinagar	400.00	Rhesus macaque, weasels, leopard, black bear, small Indian civet, red fox, wild boar, flying squirrels
		KARNATAKA		
1.	Bandipur	Mysore	874.20	Wild dog, sloth bear, jungle cat, tiger, leopard, hyena, palm civet, elephant, sambar, chital, gaur, malabar squirrel, jungle fowl, partridges.
2.	Bannerghatta	Bangalore	104.00	Sloth bear, barking deer, sambar, chital, elephant, peafowl, partridges.
3	Nagarhole	Coorg	571.55	Sloth bear, tiger, leopard, elephant, sambar, chital, gaur, malabar squirrel, jungle fowl, partridges
		KERALA		
1.	Eravikulam	Idukki	97.00	Liontailed macaque, wild dog, jungle cat, tiger, leopard, elephant, sambar, barking deer, nilgai, gaur, nilgiri tahr, malabar squirrel.
2.*	Periyar	Idukki	350.00	Liontailed macaque, nilgiri langur, wild dog, tiger, leopard, sloth bear, elephant, barking deer, sambar, mouse deer, gaur, wild boar.
3 *	Silent Valley	Palghat	344.00	Liontailed macaque, nilgiri langur, wild dog, tiger, leopard, sloth bear, elephant, barking deer, sambar, nilgai, gaur.

287

1	2	3	4	5
		MADHYA PRADESH		
1.	Bandhavgarh	Shahdol	105.00	Leopard, tiger, barking deer, sambar, chital, nilgai, chinkara, gaur, fourhorned antelope.
2.*	Indravati	Bastar	1258.00	Tiger, leopard, chital, wild buffalo, gaur.
3.	Kanha	Mandla & Balaghat	940.00	Wild dog, tiger, leopard, sambar, chital, swamp deer, blackbuck, fourhorned antelope, mouse deer, nilgai, gaur, wild boar.
4.	Madhav	Shivpuri	156.15	Hyena, tiger, leopard, sambar, chital, blackbuck, chinkara, nilgai, fourhorned antelope, crocodile.
5.*	Panna	Panna	543.00	Leopard, tiger, sambar, chital, blackbuck, nilgai, wild boar, peafowl.
6.*	Sanjay	Sidhi & Surguja	1938.00	Tiger, leopard, sambar, chital, gaur.
7.*	Satpura	Hoshangabad	524.00	Tiger, leopard, sambar, chital, blackbuck, fourhorned antelope.
8.*	Van Vihar Bhopal Zoo	Bhopal	4.41	Many species of mammals and birds.
		MAHARASHTRA		
1.	Borivili	Bombay	67.97	Hanuman langur, leopard, sambar, mouse deer, fourhorned antelope, wild boar.
2.	Nawegaon	Bhandara	133.88	Tiger, leopard, sloth bear, sambar, chital, barking deer, nilgai, gaur, migratory birds.
3.	Pench	Nagpur	257.26	Indian fox, wild dog, sloth bear, jungle cat, tiger, leopard, sambar, chital, fourhorned antelope, blackbuck, gaur.
4.	Taroba	Chandrapura	116.55	Wild dog, palm civet, jungle cat, leopard, sloth bear, sambar, chital, barking deer, gaur, wild boar, crocodile.

1	2	3	4	5
		MANIPUR		
1.	Keibul Lamjao	Manipur Central	40.00	Browantlered deer, wild boar, water birds.
2.*	Sirohi	Manipur East	41.30	—
		ORISSA		
1.	North Simlipal	Mayurbhanj	303.00	Hyena, small Indian civet, tiger, leopard, chital, mouse deer, gaur, wild boar, elephant.
		RAJASTHAN		
1.	Desert	Jaisalmer & Barmer	3162.00	Desert cat, red fox, blackbuck, chinkara, great Indian bustard, sand grouse, partridge.
2.	Keoladeo	Bharatpur	29.00	Jungle cat, sambar, chital, blackbuck, nilgai, Siberian crane, cormorant, stork, spoonbill, coot, teal, herons, tern, egrets, quail.
3.	Ranthambore	Sawai-Madhopur	392.00	Hyena, tiger, leopard, jungle cat, sambar, chital, chinkara, nilgai, partridge, green pigeon, red spurfowl.
4.*	Sariska	Alwar	492.00	Hyena, tiger, leopard, jungle cat, sambar, chital, chinkara, nilgai, fourhorned antelope, partridges.
		SIKKIM		
1.	Khangchendzonga	North Sikkim	850.00	Black bear, leopard cat, snow leopard, clouded leopard, binturong, red panda, kiang, blue sheep, serow, goral, musk deer, pheasants, partridges.
		TAMIL NADU		
1.	Guindy	Madras	2.71	Bonnet macaque, small Indian civet, chital, blackbuck, mugger, snakes.
2.*	Marine	Gulf of Mannar		—

1	2	3	4	5
		UTTAR PRADESH		
1.	Corbett	Garhwal	525.00	Black bear, tiger, leopard, jungle cat, hyena, sambar, chital, barking deer, hog deer, nilgai, peafowl, partridges, mugger, gharial, python.
2.	Dudhwa	Kheri	490.00	Tiger, leopard, sloth bear, hyena, sambar, swamp deer, chital, hog deer, barking deer, nilgai, peafowl, partridges.
3.	Nanda Devi	Chamoli	630.00	Brown bear, black bear, snow leopard, musk deer, bharal, Himalayan tahr, serow, goral, marmot, pheasants.
4.	Valley of Flowers	Chamoli	89.50	Pheasants, partridges.
		WEST BENGAL		
1.*	Sundarbans	24-Parganas	2585.00	Rhesus macaque, jackal, Indian fox, jungle cat, leopard cat, fishing cat, tiger, chital, wild boar, herons, egrets, pelican, estuarine crocodile, python.

NOTE   * Stands for preliminary notification.

LIST OF WILDLIFE SANCTUARIES IN INDIA

Sl. No.	Name	Location/ District	Area in Sq. Kms.	Important fauna
1	2	3	4	5
		ANDAMAN & NICOBAR ISLANDS		
1.	Barren Island	Bay of Bengal	8.10	Green pigeon, migratory waders.
2.	Narcondam	Bay of Bengal	6.81	Narcondam hornbill, imperial and green pigeons.
3.	North Reef	Bay of Bengal	3.40	Duck, heron, migratory waders.

1	2	3	4	5
4.	Mount Harriet	Bay of Bengal	46.62	
5.	South Sentinel	Bay of Bengal	1.61	Waders, pigeon.
		ANDHRA PRADESH		
1.	Coringa	East Godavari	235.70	Fishing cat, stork, heron, flamingo, pelican, estuarine crocodile.
2.	Eturnagaram	Warangal	803.35	Indian fox, hyena, tiger, leopard, jungle cat, chital, chinkara, fourhorned antelope, gaur, python.
3.	Kawal	Adilabad	890.00	Sloth bear, tiger, leopard, sambar, chital, blackbuck, gaur.
4.	Kinnersani	Khammam	635.40	Wolf, sloth bear, tiger, leopard, sambar, chital, gaur, mugger.
5.	Kolleru	West Godavari	673.00	Grey pelican, flamingo, heron, painted stork, avocet, teal, tern, waterfowl.
6.	Lanjamadugu	Adilabad & Karimnagar	36.21	Sloth bear, tiger, leopard, sambar, nilgai, mugger.
7.	Manjira	Medak	20.00	Mugger and water birds.
8.	Nagarjuna Sagar-Srisailam	Guntur, Prakasham, Kurnool, Mahboobnagar & Nalgonda	3568.00	Wolf, sloth bear, tiger, leopard, chital, blackbuck, nilgai, mugger.
9.	Neelapattu	Nellore	88.00	Grey pelican, heron, cormorant, teal, duck.
10	Pakhal	Warangal	860.00	Indian fox, hyena, jungle cat, tiger, leopard, chital, blackbuck, chinkara, fourhorned antelope, grey hornbill, peafowl, python.
11.	Papikonda	East Godavari, West Godavari & Khammam	590.68	Wild dog, hyena, wolf, tiger, leopard, sambar, chital, fourhorned antelope, gaur, gharial.

1	2	3	4	5
12.	Pocharam	Medak	130.13	Leopard, chital, chinkara, peafowl, water birds.
13.	Pranahita	Adilabad	136.02	Tiger, blackbuck.
14.	Pulicat	Nellore	500.00	Pelican, flamingo, stork, crane, heron, duck, teal .

ARUNACHAL PRADESH

1	2	3	4	5
1.	Itanagar	Lower Subansiri	140.80	Tiger, leopard, sloth bear, barking deer, sambar, hog deer, elephant, gaur
2.	Lali reserve forests	East Siang	190.00	Tiger, leopard, sambar, hog deer, elephant, wild buffalo, water birds, python.
3.	Mahao Reserve Forests	Dibang Valley	281.50	Leopard, sambar, hog deer, barking deer, elephant, python.
4.	Namdapha	Tirap	1907.82	Tiger, leopard, snow leopard, clouded leopard, binturong, golden cat, musk deer, hog deer, elephant, gaur, wild buffalo, flying squirrel.
5.	Pakhui Reserve Forests	East Kameng	86.00	Barking deer, sambar, hog deer, gaur, elephant, python.

ASSAM

1	2	3	4	5
1.	Barnadi	Kamrup & Darrang	26.21	Pygmy hog, hispid hare.
2.	Garampani	Sibsagar	6.00	Hoolock gibbon, leopard, elephant, wild buffalo, whitewinged wood duck.
3	Laokhowa	Nowgong	70.00	Swamp deer, hog deer, rhinoceros, wild buffalo, cormorant, ducks.
4.	Manas Tiger Reserve	Kamrup & Goalpara	390.00	Golden langur, Indian fox, black bear, leopard cat, tiger, leopard, swamp deer, hog deer, rhinoceros, elephant, gaur, wild buffalo, pygmy hog, hispid hare, great pied hornbill, florican, python.

1	2	3	4	5
5.	Orang	Darrang	72.59	Tiger, leopard, sambar, swamp deer, elephant, onehorned rhinoceros, whistling teal, florican, quail, green pigeon, geese.
6.	Pabha	Lakhimpur	49.00	Barking deer, wild buffalo, elephant.
7.	Pabitora Game Reserve	Nowgong	16.00	
8.	Sonai Rupa	Darrang	175.00	Sloth bear, tiger, leopard, sambar, swamp deer elephant, rhinoceros, wild buffalo, gaur, hornbill, imperial pigeon.

BIHAR

1	2	3	4	5
1.	Bhimbandh	Monghyr	631.90	Wolf, tiger, leopard, sambar, chital, wild boar, water birds.
2.	Dalma	Singhbhum	193.22	Sloth bear, leopard, barking deer, mouse deer, wild boar.
3.	Gautam Buddha	Gaya	259.50	Tiger, leopard, barking deer, sambar, chital, peafowl.
4.	Hazaribagh	Hazaribagh	186.25	Indian fox, jungle cat, tiger, leopard, barking deer, sambar, chital, nilgai, wild boar, peafowl.
5.	Kaimur	Rohtas	1342.22	Tiger, leopard, barking deer, sambar, nilgai, crocodile.
6.	Lawalong	Hazaribagh	207.00	Sloth bear, tiger, leopard, sambar, chital.
7.	Mahuadaur	Palamau	63.25	Wolf, tiger, leopard, barking deer, chital, wild boar.
8.	Palamau Tiger Reserve	Palamau	979.27	Hyena, palm civet, tiger, leopard, elephant, sambar, chital, barking deer, gaur, wild boar, peafowl, partridge, jungle fowl.
9.	Rajgir	Nalanda	35.84	Tiger, leopard, sambar, chital, barking deer.
10.	Topchanchi	Dhanbad	8.75	Ducks, water fowl.
11.	Udaipur	Champaran	6.57	Wolf, tiger, leopard, sambar, chital, nilgai.
12.	Valmikinagar	Champaran	148.55	Tiger, leopard, sambar, chital.

293

1	2	3	4	5
		CHANDIGARH		
1.	Sukhna	Chandigarh	25.40	Migratory and endemic birds.
		GOA, DAMAN & DIU		
1.	Bhagvan Mahavir	Goa	240.00	Tiger, leopard, small Indian civet, barking deer, sambar, chital, mouse deer, gaur, malabar squirrel, hornbill.
2.	Bondla	Goa	8.00	Leopard, small Indian civet, sambar, mouse deer, fourhorned antelope, wild boar.
3.	Cotigao	Goa	105.00	Slender Loris, Hanuman langur, leopard, sambar, gaur, malabar squirrel.
		GUJARAT		
1.	Barda	Jamnagar	192.31	Asiatic lion, chital, chinkara, python.
2.	Dhumkhal	Broach	150.87	Sloth bear.
3.	Gir Lion Sanctuary	Junagadh	1265.01	Hyena, Asiatic lion, leopard, sambar, chital, chinkara, fourhorned antelope, python, muger.
4.	Hingolgadhan	Rajkot	6.54	
5.	Jessore	Banaskantha	180.66	Sloth bear, leopard, chital.
6.	Khijadiya	Jamnagar	4.23	Water birds.
7.	Marine.	Jamnagar	271.32	Common dolphin, sea turtle, fishes, molluscs, crustaceans, coelenterates.
8.	Nalsarovar	Ahmedabad & Surendranagar	115.00	Flamingo, grey pelican, painted stork, spoonbill, pond heron, black ibis, moorhen, coot, waterfowl.
9.	Narayan Sarovar	Kutch	765.79	Chinkara, nilgai.
10.	Ratanmahal	Panch Mahals	55.65	—
11.	Wild Ass Sanctuary	Surendranagar	49.53	Red fox, wolf, chinkara, nilgai, wild ass, flamingo.

1	2	3	4	5
		HARYANA		
1.	Sultanpur	Gurgaon	1.44	Water birds (resident and migratory)
		HIMACHAL PRADESH		
1.	Bandli	Mandi	41.32	Black bear, leopard, snow leopard, marten, goral, pheasants.
2.	Chail	Solan	23.22	Barking deer, goral.
3.	Daranghati I & II	Simla	167.40	Black bear, marten, leopard, goral, serow, pheasants
4.	Darlaghat	Solan	44.32	Leopard, snow leopard, marten, goral, partridges, pheasants.
5.	Gamgul Siya Behi	Chamba	9.00	Brown and black bears, marten, leopard, musk deer, hangul, goral, Himalayan tahr, snowcock, pheasants
6.	Gobindsagar	Bilaspur	100.34	Crane, duck, goose, teal.
7.	Kalatop & Khajjiar	Chamba	47.28	Red fox, black bear, snow leopard, leopard, marten, goral, serow, bharal, pheasants.
8.	Kanswar	Kulu	54.27	Black bear, leopard, Himalayan tahr, serow, goral, partridges, pheasants.
9.	Khokhan	Kulu	13.36	Black bear, leopard, Himalayan tahr, serow, goral, partridges, pheasants.
10.	Kias	Kulu	13.65	Black bear, leopard, Himalayan tahr, serow, goral, partridges, pheasants.
11.	Kugti	Chamba	118.29	Brown and black bears, leopard, snow leopard, marten, musk deer, Himalayan tahr, goral, serow, ibex, partridges, pheasants.
12.	Lippa Asrang	Kinnaur	109.11	Leopard, marten, ibex, bharal, goral, snowcock, pheasants.

1	2	3	4	5
13.	Majathal & Hasrang	Solan	92.06	Red fox, black bear, leopard, snow leopard, goral, partridges, pheasants.
14.	Manali	Kulu	28.37	Black bear, leopard, Himalayan tahr, serow, goral partridges, pheasants.
15.	Neggu	Mandi	278.38	Red fox, black bear, leopard, snow leopard, marten musk deer, goral, serow, patridges, pheasants.
16.	Raksham Chitkul	Kinnaur	138.44	Black bear, brown bear, marten, red fox, leopard, ibex bharal, goral, pheasants.
17.	Renuka	Sirmur	13.44	Leopard, barking deer, sambar, goral, peafowl, red jungle fowl, partridges.
18.	Sechutun Nala	Chamba	4.14	Red fox, brown bear, black bear, snow leopard, leopard, lynx, marten, ibex, Himalayan tahr, goral, serow, musk deer, snowcock, pheasants.
19.	Shikari Devi	Mandi	213.51	Black bear, leopard, snow leopard, marten, musk deer, goral, serow, pheasants.
20.	Shilli	Solan	1.97	Red fox, marten, leopard, snow leopard, barking deer, partridges, pheasants.
21.	Simbalbara	Sirmur	55.37	Leopard, barking deer, sambar, goral, red jungle fowl, partridges, pheasants.
22.	Sri Naina Devi	Bilaspur	163.38	Black bear, marten, leopard, snow leopard, sambar, barking deer, nilgai, patridge.
23.	Ruppi Bhawa	Kinnaur	124.87	Black bear, red fox, marten, leopard, goral, partridges, pheasants.
24.	Talra	Simla	76.20	Black bear, marten, leopard, musk deer, sambar, goral, pheasants.
25.	Tirthan	Kulu	83.96	Black bear, leopard, goral.

1	2	3	4	5
26.	Tundah	Chamba	64.22	Red fox, marten, weasel, brown and black bears, snow leopard, leopard, Himalayan tahr, goral, serow, ibex, musk deer, pheasants.
27.	Water Supply Catchment Area	Simla	10.25	Leopard, snow leopard, marten, barking deer, goral, serow, pheasants.

JAMMU AND KASHMIR

1	2	3	4	5
1.	Nandini	Jammu	33.34	Rhesus macaque, black bear, small Indian civet, jungle cat, Indian grey mongoose, goral, flying squirrel, paradise flycatcher, starling.
2.	Overa	Srinagar	60.00	Rhesus macaque, hanuman langur, red fox, brown bear, black bear, leopard, chakor.
3.	Ramnagar Rakh	Jammu	12.20	Rhesus macaque, black bear, small Indian civet, jungle cat, Indian grey mongoose, goral, flying squirrel, paradise flycatcher, starling.
4.	Surinsar & Mansar Patwar	Jammu	39.13	Rhesus macaque, black bear, small Indian civet, jungle cat, Indian grey mongoose, goral, flying squirrel, paradise flycatcher, starling.

KARNATAKA

1	2	3	4	5
1.	Adichuncha Nagiri	Mandya	—	Peafowl
2.	Arabithitto	Mysore	13.50	Chital, wild boar, porcupine, hare, peafowl, quail, partridge.
3.	Bhadra	Shimoga & Chikmagalur	506.00	Sloth bear, tiger, leopard, sambar, chital, wild boar gaur, elephant.
4.	Biligiri Rangaswamy	Mysore	324.40	Sloth bear, leopard, barking deer, sambar, chital elephant.
5.	Brahmagiri	Coorg	181.29	Sloth bear, tiger, leopard, barking deer, sambar, chital, mouse deer, malabar squirrel.

297

1	2	3	4	5
6.	Dandeli	Dharwar	572.90	Sloth bear, tiger, leopard, palm civet, sambar, chital, gaur, wild boar, flying squirrel.
7.	Ghataprabha	Belgaum	29.78	Egrets, cormorant, herons and other water birds.
8.	Melkota Temple	Mandya	49.82	Sloth bear, wolf, leopard, blackbuck, wild boar, hare, porcupine.
9.	Mokambika	Shimoga	254.09	Leopard, sambar, elephant, wild boar.
10.	Nagu	Mysore	30.32	Tiger, barking deer, sambar, chital, gaur, wild boar, elephant.
11.	Ranebennur	Dharwar.	119.00	Blackbuck.
12.	Ranganthittoo	Mysore	26.67	Openbilled stork, white ibis, little egret, darter, pelican, cormorant, pond heron, spoonbill, tern, crocodile
13.	Setthalli	Shimoga	406.86	Sloth bear, leopard, barking deer, sambar, chital, gaur, wild boar, elephant.
14.	Sharawathy Valley	Shimoga	442.67	Liontailed monkey, wild dog, tiger, leopard, sloth bear, barking deer, sambar, chital, fourhorned antelope, elephant, crocodile.
15.	Someshwara	Shimoga	90.86	Sloth bear, tiger, leopard, wild dog, sambar, chital, gaur.
16.	Tungabhadra	Shimoga	224.22	Sloth bear, leopard, sambar, chital, blackbuck, fourhorned antelope, sand grouse, florican.
		KERALA		
1	Idukki	Idukki	70.00	Sloth bear, elephant, sambar, gaur, wild boar.
2	Neyyar	Trivandrum	128.00	Sloth bear, tiger, leopard, elephant, sambar, chital, nilgai, mugger

1	2	3	4	5
3.	Parambikulam	Palghat	270.00	Sloth bear, tiger, leopard, elephant, sambar, chital, nilgai, gaur, mugger.
4.	Poochi Vazhani	Trichur	125.00	Elephant, chital.
5.	Wyanad	Kozhikode Cannanore	344.00	Elephant, barking deer, sambar, chital, gaur.
		MADHYA PRADESH		
1.	Achanakmar	Bilaspur	551.55	Tiger, sambar, chital, gaur, wild boar, peafowl.
2.	Badalkhol	Raigarh	104.45	Tiger, leopard, sambar, chital, nilgai.
3.	Bagdara	Sidhi	478.00	Leopard, sambar, blackbuck, chinkara, wild boar.
4.	Barnawapara	Raipur	244.66	Tiger, leopard, barking deer, sambar, chital, gaur, hare.
5.	Bori	Hoshangabad	518.00	Tiger, leopard, barking deer, sambar, chital, chinkara, gaur, wild boar.
6.	Chambal	Morena	3582.00	Gharial.
7.	Gandhisagar	Mandsaur	225.00	Chital, barking deer, chinkara, water birds.
8.	Ghatigaon	Gwalior	512.00	Great Indian bustard, partridges.
9.	Gomarda	Raigarh	136.38	Tiger, leopard, barking deer, sambar, chital, gaur.
10.	Karera	Shivpuri	202.00	Great Indian bustard, partridges.
11.	Ken Gharial Sanctuary	Panna & Chhatarpur	45.00	Gharial.
12.	Kheoni	Dewas	123.00	Leopard, sloth bear, sambar, chital, nilgai.
13.	Narsingarh	Rajgarh	57.20	Leopard, sambar, chital, wild boar, peafowl.
14.	Noradehi	Sagar, Damoh & Narsimhapur	1035.00	Tiger, leopard, sambar, chital, chinkara, nilgai.
15.	Pachmarhi	Hoshangabad	461.84	Tiger, leopard, sloth bear, barking deer, sambar, chital, gaur.
16.	Palpur (Kuno)	Morena	345.00	—
17.	Pench	Seoni & Chhindwara	449.39	Tiger, leopard, sambar, chital, nilgai, gaur.

1	2	3	4	5
18	Ratapani	Raisen	530.67	Tiger, leopard, sambar, chital, nilgai, chinkara
19	Semarsot	Surguja	430.00	Tiger, leopard, sambar, chital, gaur.
20	Sindhori	Raisen	287.91	Tiger, leopard, sambar, chital, nilgai, gaur.
21	Sitanadi	Raipur	553.00	Tiger, leopard, sambar, chital, gaur, wild boar, peafowl
22	Son Gharial Sanctuary	Sidhi, Shahdol & Satna	20.00	Gharial.
23	Tamor Pigla	Surguja	608.53	Tiger, leopard, sambar, chital, gaur.

MAHARASHTRA

1	2	3	4	5
1	Bor	Wardha	61.10	Leopard, sloth bear, barking deer, sambar, chital, chinkara, wild boar.
2	Deulgaon Dehekuri	Ahmadnagar	2.17	Blackbuck, chinkara, partridges.
3	Dhakna Kolkaz	Amravati	381.58	Tiger, leopard, barking deer, sambar, chital, fourhorned antelope, gaur.
4	Great Indian Bustard Sanctuary	Ahmadnagar	7818.47	Great Indian bustard, partridges.
5	Karnala	Raigad	4.48	Leopard, fourhorned antelope, ashy minivet, paradise flycatcher, malabar whistling thrush, racket-tailed drongo, woodpecker, water birds
6	Kinwat	Yeotmal & Nanded	38.00	Tiger, leopard, sloth bear, barking deer, sambar, chital, chinkara, wild boar.
7	Nagzira	Bhandara	136.14	Tiger, leopard, sloth bear, barking deer, sambar, chital, mouse deer, nilgai, gaur, fourhorned antelope
8	Radhanagari	Kolhapur	2072.00	Leopard, sambar, blackbuck, gaur.
9	Tansa	Thana	216.75	Leopard, sambar, blackbuck, gaur.
10	Yawal	Jalgaon	177.52	Tiger, leopard, wild dog, hyena, jungle cat, chital, chinkara, peafowl, partridges.

1	2	3	4	5
		MEGHALAYA		
1.	Nongkhyllem	United Khasi & Jaintia Hills	24.00	—
2.	Siju	Garo Hills	5.18	Many kinds of bats, rats and snakes.
		MIZORAM		
1.	Dampa	Aizawal	973.46	Tiger, leopard, bear, sambar, barking deer, gaur, elephant.
		NAGALAND		
1.	Intangki	Kohima	202.02	Leopard, tiger, clouded leopard, bear, elephant, barking deer, gaur, pangolin.
2.	Pulicbadze	Kohima	9.23	—
		ORISSA		
1.	Bhittar Kanika	Cuttack	170.00	Hyena, jungle cat, leopard, chital, sambar, storks, ibises, estuarine crocodile, sea turtle.
2.	Chandka	Puri	30.00	Leopard, sloth bear, chital, elephant.
3.	Hadgarh	Keonjhar & Mayurbhanj	191.60	Chital, elephant, peafowl, crocodile.
4.	Khalasuni	Sambalpur	116.00	Sloth bear, elephant, sambar, chital, gaur.
5.	Kothgarh	Baud-khondmals	3995.00	Tiger, leopard, sloth bear, elephant, chital.
6.	Mahanadi baisipalli	Puri	168.35	—
7.	Nandankanan Biological Park	Puri	14.02	Many kinds of mammals and birds, crocodiles.
8.	Satkosia Gorge	Dhenkanal, Puri, Cuttack & Baud-Khondmals	795.52	Sloth bear, tiger, leopard, sambar, chital, nilgai, fourhorned antelope, gharial.
9.	Simlipal	Mayurbhanj	2750.00	Hyena, tiger, leopard, small Indian civet, elephant, chital, mouse deer, gaur, flying squirrel.

1	2	3	4	5
		PUNJAB		
1.	Abohar	Ferozepur	18.8	Blackbuck, hare, partridges, doves.
2.	Bir Bunerheri	Patiala	8.2	Hog deer, nilgai, wild boar, hare, peafowl, partridges, woodpecker.
3.	Bir Gurdial Pura	Patiala	8.4	
4.	Bir Motibagh Patiala	Patiala	5.2	Hog deer, nilgai, wild boar, hare, peafowl, partridges, woodpecker.
		RAJASTHAN		
1.	Bhensroad Garh	Chitorgarh	—	
2.	Darrah	Kota	201.00	Tiger, leopard, sloth bear, sambar, chital, nilgai, chinkara, wild boar, partridge, sand grouse.
3.	Jaisamand	Udaipur	52.00	Leopard, sloth bear, sambar, chital, chinkara, nilgai, partridge, quail, spurfowl.
4.	Jamwa Ramgarh	Jaipur	300.00	
5.	Jawahar Sagar	Kota	100.00	Chinkara, gharial.
6.	Kumbhalgarh	Udaipur	500.00	Leopard, sambar, nilgai, jungle fowl, red spurfowl.
7.	Mt. Abu	Sirohi	112.60	Langur, hyena, leopard, sloth bear, sambar, chinkara, partridge, jungle fowl.
8.	National chambal	Kota	280.00	Gharial.
9.	Ramgarh Vishdhari	Bundi	307.00	
10.	Sita Mata	Udaipur	500.00	Blackbuck, chinkara, partridge.
11.	Tal Chapper	Churu	8.00	Blackbuck.
12.	Van Vihar	Dholpur	59.00	Tiger, leopard, sambar, chital, chinkara, nilgai, partridge, peafowl.

1	2	3	4	5
		TAMIL NADU		
1.	Anaimalai	Coimbatore	958.60	Lion-tailed macaque, nilgiri langur, tiger, leopard, wild dog, sloth bear, elephant, sambar, chital, nilgiri tahr, gaur.
2.	Kalkad	Tirunelveli	223.58	Lion-tailed macaque.
3.	Karikili	Chingleput	—	Cormorants, dabchick, egrets, comb duck, moorhen, ibis, pelican, stork, spoonbill.
4.	Mudumalai	Nilgiris	321.00	Wild dog, hyena, sloth bear, tiger, leopard, jungle cat, elephant, sambar, chital, barking deer, mouse deer, fourhorned antelope, gaur.
5.	Mundanthurai	Tirunelveli	567.38	Lion-tailed macaque, nilgiri langur, wild dog, tiger, leopard, sloth bear, sambar, chital, barking deer, mouse deer.
6.	Nilgiri Tahr Sanctuary	Nilgiris	78.46	Nilgiri Tahr.
7.	Point Calimere	Thanjavur	254.35	Bonnet macaque, small Indian civet, chital, blackbuck, wild boar.
8.	Pulicat	Chingleput	—	Cormorants, dabchick, egrets, comb duck, moorhen, ibis, pelican, stork, spoonbill.
9.	Vedanthangal	Chingleput	—	Cormorants, dabchick, egrets, comb duck, moorhen, ibis, pelican, stork, spoonbill.
		UTTAR PRADESH		
1.	Chandra Prabha	Varanasi	78.00	Leopard, sloth bear, sambar, chital, chinkara, nilgai, wild boar, partridge, peafowl.
2.	Chila	Garhwal	249.00	Sloth bear, tiger, leopard, elephant, sambar, chital, nilgai, goral.

303

1	2	3	4	5
3.	Govind Pashuvihar	Uttarkashi	953.00	Brown bear, black bear, snow leopard, musk deer, sambar, bharal, serow, goral, Himalayan tahr, pheasants.
4.	Kaimur	Mirzapur	500.75	Tiger, leopard, caracal, chital, sambar, python, cobra
5.	Keterniaghat	Bahraich	400.00	Tiger, leopard, sloth bear, sambar, chital, blackbuck, gharial.
6.	Kedarnath	Chamoli	957.00	Brown bear, snow leopard, musk deer, bharal, serow, goral, Himalayan tahr, pheasants.
7.	Kishanpur	Kheri	227.12	Tiger, leopard, sambar, chital, barking deer, peafowl, red jungle fowl.
8.	Mahavir Swami	Lalitpur	54.00	Sloth bear, leopard, sambar, chital, chinkara, blackbuck.
9.	Motichur	Dehra Dun	89.50	Tiger, leopard, elephant, sambar, chital peafowl, red jungle fowl.
10.	National Chambal	Lalitpur	635.00	Gharial.
11.	Rajaji	Saharanpur.	247.00	Tiger, leopard, sloth bear, elephant, barking deer, sambar, chital, nilgai, wild boar, pheasants, partridges.
12.	Ranipur	Banda	250.00	Hyena, Indian fox, jungle cat, tiger, leopard, sambar, chital, chinkara, blackbuck.
	WEST BENGAL			
1.	Ballavpur Deer Park	Birbhum	0.82	Chital, blackbuck.
2.	Bethuadahari	Nadia	0.67	Sambar, chital, barking deer.
3.	Chapramari	Jalpaiguri	8.80	Tiger, elephant, barking deer, sambar, gaur, variety of birds.
4.	Gorumara	Jalpaiguri	8.62	Tiger, elephant, onehorned rhinoceros, sambar, hog deer, gaur, peafowl.

1	2	3	4	5
5.	Halliday	24-Parganas	5.96	Tiger, chital, water birds.
6.	Jaldapara	Jalpaiguri	115.00	Rhesus monkey, tiger, leopard, jungle cat, sloth bear, elephant, onehorned rhinoceros, sambar, barking deer, hog deer, gaur.
7.	Lothian Island	24-Parganas	37.96	Tiger, otter, chital, wild boar, gangetic dolphin, estuarine crocodile, water birds.
8.	Mahananda	Darjiling	127.22	Hanuman langur, Assamese macaque, tiger, elephant, sambar, hog deer, barking deer.
9.	Narendrapur	24-Parganas	20.50	A variety of birds.
10.	Parmadan Deer Park	24-Parganas	0.64	Chital.
11.	Ramnabagan	Bardhaman	1.43	
12.	Sajnakhali	24-Parganas	362.33	Tiger, chital, stork, egrets, herons, cormorant, pelican, ibis.
13.	Senchal	Darjiling	39.54	Wild dog, black bear, barking deer, serow, goral, pheasants.

Addresses to which enquiries should be sent by persons intending to visit India's wildlife places

ANDHRA PELICANRY	The Chief Conservator of Forests, Hyderabad, Andhra Pradesh, India.
BANDIPUR	The Divisional Forest Officer, Mysore City, Karnataka, India.
BHARATPUR	The Divisional Forest Officer, Bharatpur, Rajasthan, India.
CHANDRAPRABHA	The Divisional Forest Officer, Varanasi Division, Ramnagar, Uttar Pradesh, India.
CORBETT	The Chief Wild Life Warden, Wazir Hassan Road. Lucknow Uttar Pradesh, India.
DACHIGAM	The Chief Conservator of Forests, Srinagar, Jammu & Kashmir, India.
GIR FOREST	The Divisional Forest Officer, Gir Division, Junagadh, Gujarat, India.
HAZARIBAGH	The Divisional Forest Officer, Hazaribagh Division, Bihar, India.
JALDAPARA	The Divisional Forest Officer, Cooch Behar, West Bengal, India.
KANHA	The Divisional Forest Officer, West Mandla Division, Mandla, Madhya Pradesh, India.
KAZIRANGA	The Divisional Forest Officer, Sibsagar Division, Jorhat, Assam, India.
KUTCH	The Divisional Forest Officer, Bhuj, Kutch, Gujarat, India.
MADUMALAI	The State Wild Life Officer, 136, Peters Road, Madras-14, India.
MANAS	The Divisional Forest Officer, North Kamrup Division, Barpeta Road, Assam, India.
PERIYAR	The Wild Life Warden, Peermade, Kerala, India.
RANGANTHITTOO	The Divisional Forest Officer, Mysore City, Karnataka, India.
SHIVPURI	The Divisional Forest Officer, Shivpuri, Madhya Pradesh, India.
VEDANTHANGAL	The State Wild Life Officer, 136, Peters Road, Madras-14, India.

IMPORTANT SANCTUARIES OF INDIA

(The best months of the year for visiting)

	Best time	Second best time
Bandipur, KARNATAKA	April — May	February — March and November — December
Ranganthittoo, KARNATAKA	July & August	June
Mudumalai, TAMIL NADU	February — May	November — December
Vedanthangal, TAMIL NADU	January & December	February & November
Periyar, KERALA	January — March	April — May
Bharatpur, RAJASTHAN	August — October	July
Kanha, M.P.	April — May	February, March & June
Shivpuri, M.P.	February & July	March — June
Gir Forest, GUJARAT	January — May	December
Chandraprabha, U.P	February — April	January & May
Corbett, U.P.	March & April	February & May
Dachigam, J & K	May — October	January & December
Hazaribagh, BIHAR	February — May	January & December
Jaldapara, WEST BENGAL	February — April	January & December
Manas, ASSAM	January — March	November & December
Kaziranga, ASSAM	January — April	November & December

We must try to preserve whatever is left of our forests and the wild life that inhabits them"

— Jawaharlal Nehru

The End